50 Bible Paper Pop-Ups

3-D Visuals for Hands-On Learning Fun

Developed by Robin S. Parimore
Illustrated by Lynne Marie Davis

STANDARD PUBLISHING
Cincinnati, Ohio

50 Bible Paper Pop-Ups

With instructional sketches by Robin S. Parimore
Cover design by Roberta K. Loman

The Standard Publishing Company, Cincinnati, Ohio. A division of Standex International Corporation.
©1996 by The Standard Publishing Company. All rights reserved. Printed in the United States of America.

ISBN 0-7847-0484-8

03 02 01 00 99 98 97 96   5 4 3 2 1

New Testament

Basic Tips

Paper

- Choose bright, appropriate colors of construction paper for the paper-fold cards.
- The construction paper for most cards will be folded in half to make a 6-by-9-inch card. Several cards will be folded lengthwise and some will use only a half-sheet of construction paper folded to make a 4 1/2-by-6-inch card. See individual instructions.
- For best results, use 24-lb. photocopy paper (called *heavyweight copy paper* in this book). It is thicker and stiffer than standard copy paper, and it holds a fold more crisply than most construction papers. Also called resume paper, it is readily available at office supply stores.
- Several activities use medium-weight poster board.

Glue and Tape

- Use glue sticks. Glue sticks are easy for small hands to handle and they do not spill! One swipe of a glue stick gives good coverage on the glue tabs in this book. If glue is put in the wrong place, allow it to dry. (Blow on it—this glue dries quickly.) Rub glue with your finger. It will ball up and come off completely and easily.
- Use clear adhesive tape to reinforce the back of slits, weak areas, and paper-fastener and hole-punch areas so they won't tear.

Folding and Cutting Shapes

- Use a .5 mm mechanical pencil (with lead retracted) and a ruler to make scoring all fold lines quick and easy. Tip: An empty ball-point pen can also be used.
- Score photocopied activities *before* cutting out.
- The dot lines (for mountain folds) and dash lines (for valley folds) showing at the top and bottom of a shape indicate a fold down the center. Line up a ruler with the top and bottom fold lines and score.
- Use a cutting mat with an X-Acto knife. Mats save blades and make cutting easier. (Cardboard tablet-backing makes an acceptable mat.)
- Stack three or four papers of the same shape, staple, and cut out all at the same time.
- Use an X-Acto knife to cut an **X** in the paper where brads insert. Children can put them in more easily.
- When a shape must be cut from construction paper, photocopy the reproducible page, cut out the pattern for that shape, trace it onto construction paper and cut out. Score.
- When a shape must be placed on a fold, begin by folding the construction paper. Trace the pattern onto the construction paper aligning the place-on-fold edge of the pattern with the folded edge of the construction paper. Cut out. Score.

Plus . . .

- It will help to provide a completed example for children to see.
- Samples and leftover visual activities store flat in file folders. They'll be easy to find later!
- Follow the **Preschool** instructions with younger children or to save class time.

See page 7 for list of basic supplies and materials.

Pop-Ups With Tabs

2, 3, 49

- Score photocopied shapes along all dot/dash fold lines. Cut out. Fold.
- Fold and crease a sheet of construction paper in half. This is your card.
- Open card. With shape folded flat, glue the back of tab on the right side and place it on the right side of card making sure to keep entire shape within card. See **1.** Make sure the inside edge of tab is aligned with the center crease of card.
- Glue the side of the tab facing up and close.
- When card is opened, activity stands up. See **2.**

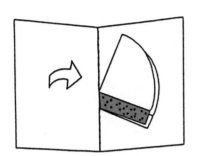 **1**   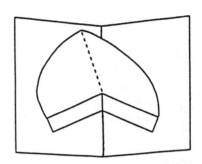 **2**

Pop-Ups in a Picture

5, 19, 24, 39

- Score photocopied shape along all dot/dash fold lines. Cut out. Fold. See **1.**
- Fold and crease one sheet of construction paper in half. This is your card.
- Open card. With shape folded flat, glue the back of the right side of shape where indicated and place on the right side of card. See **2.** Since there are no designated tabs on these examples, refer to specific item instructions for area to glue. Make sure to align center of shape with the center crease of card. Some have one **V**-fold, facing up or down. Others have two **V**-folds. **V**-folds are always *pulled* to the inside of card.
- Glue the side of shape facing up, where indicated, and close.
- When card is opened, activity pops out. See **3.**

1 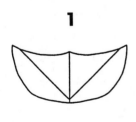   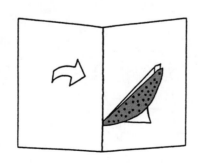 **2**   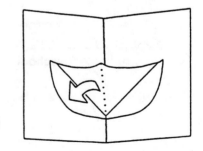 **3**

Box Stand-Ups

4, 14, 30, 44

- Score photocopied shape along all dot/dash fold lines. Cut out. Fold.
- Fold and crease one sheet of construction paper in half. This is your card.
- Open card. Glue bottom tab of shape and line up bottom edge with center crease of card. See **1.**
- Lay the shape flat with top two sections folded back. See **1.** Glue top tab and close card.
- When card is opened halfway, activity will stand up. See **2.** When card is opened flat, activity will also lie flat.

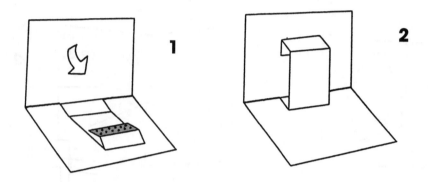

Stand-Up Animals

15, 41

- Score photocopied animals. Cut out. Use an X-Acto knife to cut out area under heads. (Tabs at feet or belly are not shown in this example.)
- Fold animal along its back (center), wrong sides together.
- To form figures, the back fold stays the same (valley) and the head fold is reversed. Head and neck folds are mountain folds. When you pull the head out and back, score lines at neck will help to pop head up into place. See **1.** When formed correctly, the photocopied side of head will show. See **2.**
- Glue tabs on animals as directed in specific instructions.

Box Support

22, 29

- Cut out photocopied support. Score and fold on dotted lines (mountain folds) to form an open-ended box.
- Glue photocopied support onto construction paper for stability. Cut out.
- Fold and crease one sheet of construction paper in half. This is your card.
- Open the card. Fold support as shown and glue the two ends of the folded support. See 1. Place support on the card so that the ends of the support meet along the center crease of the card. See **2**. Close and press.
- When card is opened halfway, support will be square. When card is opened flat, support will also lie flat.
- Glue support on one side and place photocopied shape on it, making sure that the bottom of the shape is not lower than the bottom of the support. See **3**. Close and press.

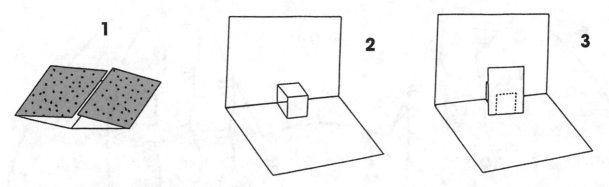

Supplies and Materials

Using these few basic supplies and materials, preschool and primary children can create memorable pop-up Bible visuals.

construction paper
24-lb. copy paper
sharp scissors
glue stick
crayons
clear adhesive tape
ruler

.5 mm mechanical pencil
   or other scoring tool
hole punch
X-Acto knife
cutting mat
stapler
paper fasteners (brads)

yarn or string
Special materials are
   required for a few crafts
   (rubber bands, chenille
   stems, star stickers).

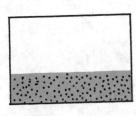

Glue stick

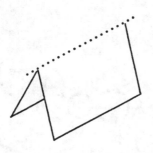

Mountain folds indicated by

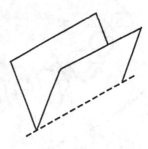

Valley folds indicated by

Genesis 1, 2

Creation

Before Class
- Photocopy **1A** and **1B** onto white, heavyweight copy paper. Use an X-Acto knife to cut out the two areas on **1A**.
- Make a small **X** with an X-Acto knife at the center of **1A** and **1B**.

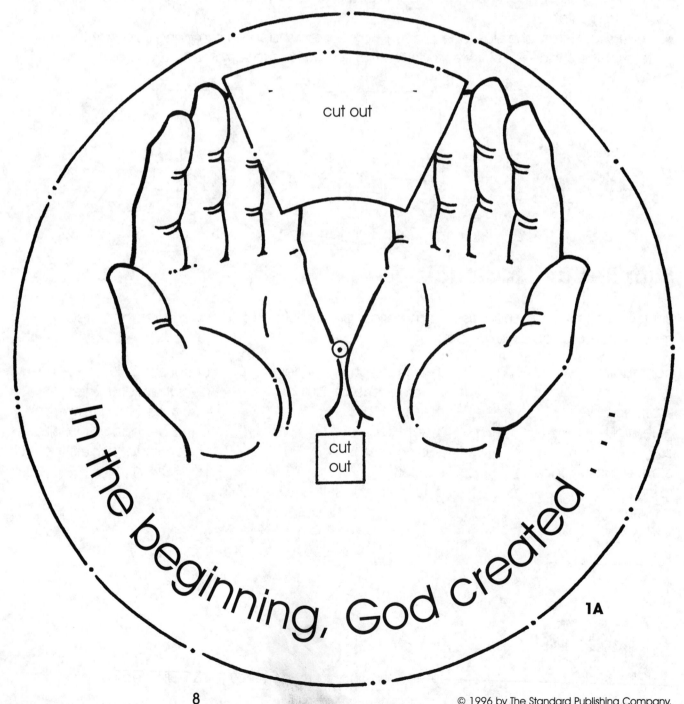

cut out

cut out

In the beginning, God created . . .

1A

8

© 1996 by The Standard Publishing Company.
Permission is granted to reproduce this page for ministry purposes only—not for resale.

In • Have children color **1A** and **1B**.
Class • Insert the paper fastener through the center with **1A** on top of **1B**.

Materials for one activity
2 sheets white, heavyweight copy paper
1 paper fastener (brad)
X-Acto knife
scissors
crayons

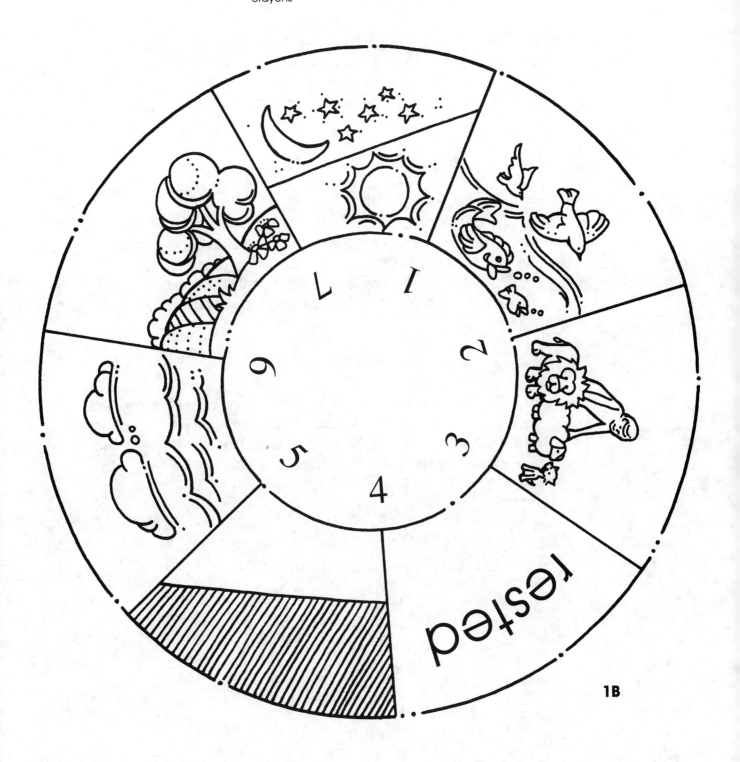

© 1996 by The Standard Publishing Company.
Permission is granted to reproduce this page for ministry purposes only—not for resale.

Rainbow in the Sky

Before Class
- Photocopy reproducible page onto white, heavyweight copy paper. Score all fold lines. Cut out each piece.
- Fold all dash lines (valley) on rainbow **(2A).**
- Fold and crease one sheet of construction paper in half. This is your card.

In Class

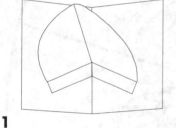

- Have children color each piece.
- Follow instructions **Pop-Ups With Tabs** (page 5). See **1.**
- Glue cloud **(2B)** onto the top edge of rainbow.
- Glue **2C** to outside and **2D** to inside of card.
- When children open their cards, a rainbow pops up.

1

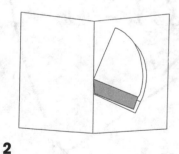

Preschool

Before class, have rainbow glued to one side of inside of card. See **2.** In class, children can open card and rainbow flat, color it, glue cloud on rainbow. Fold rainbow back up as it was. Have children glue tab facing up. Close card and press.

2

Materials for one activity
1 sheet construction paper
1 sheet white, heavyweight copy paper
scissors
glue stick
crayons

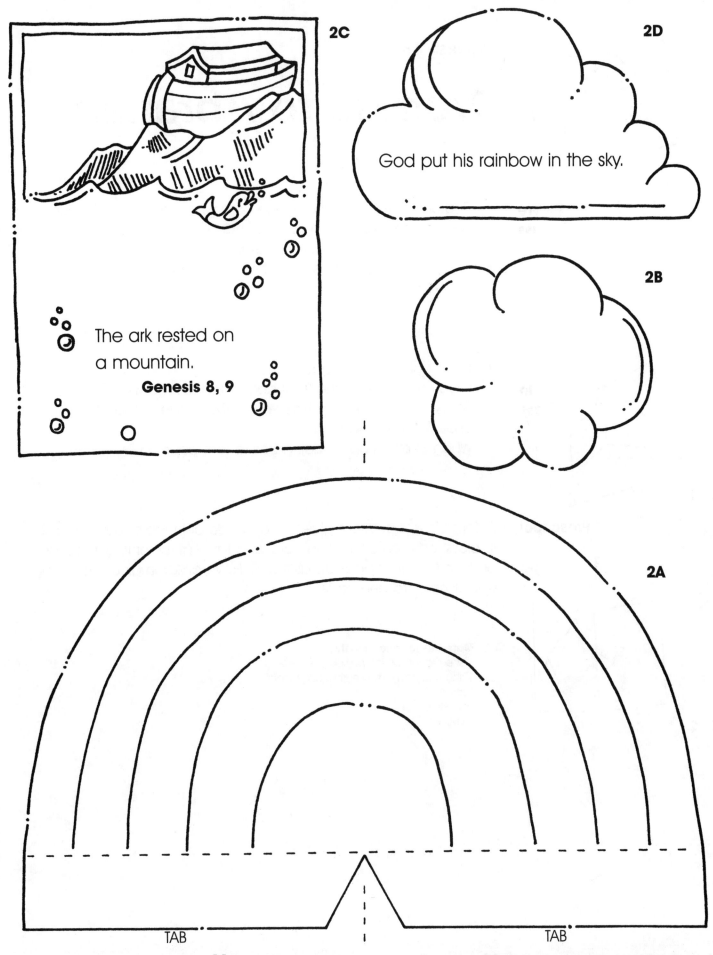

2C

2D

God put his rainbow in the sky.

2B

The ark rested on
a mountain.
Genesis 8, 9

2A

TAB

TAB

© 1996 by The Standard Publishing Company.
Permission is granted to reproduce this page for ministry purposes only—not for resale.

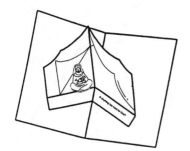

Promise to Abraham

Before Class
- Photocopy reproducible page onto white, heavyweight copy paper. Score all fold lines on tent **(3A).** Cut out each piece.
- Fold all dash lines (valley) on tent.
- Fold and crease one sheet of construction paper in half. This is your card.

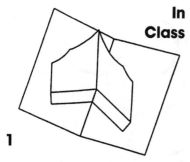

In Class
- Have children color each piece.
- Glue Sarah **(3B)** to the front side of tent as shown.
- Follow instructions **Pop-Ups With Tabs** (page 5). See **1.**
- Glue **3C** to outside of card.
- When children open their cards, a tent pops up.

1

Preschool

Before class, have tent glued to one side of inside of card. See **2.** In class, children can open card and tent flat, color it, glue Sarah on tent. Fold tent back up as it was. Have children glue tab facing up. Close card and press.

Materials for one activity
1 sheet construction paper
1 sheet white, heavyweight copy paper
scissors
glue stick
crayons

2

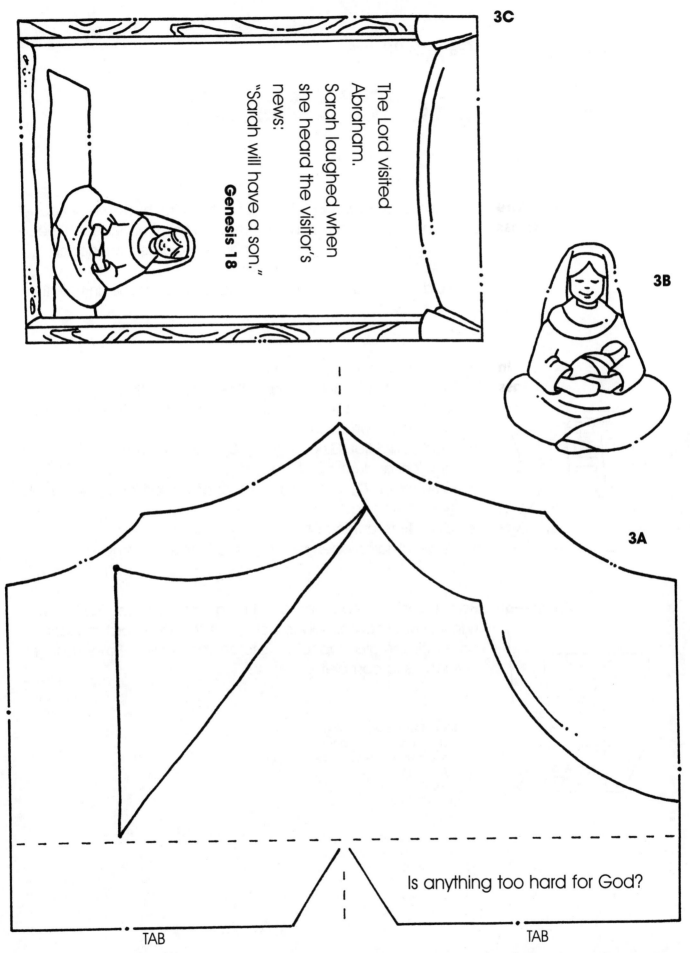

3C

The Lord visited Abraham. Sarah laughed when she heard the visitor's news: "Sarah will have a son."

Genesis 18

3B

3A

Is anything too hard for God?

TAB   TAB

13

© 1996 by The Standard Publishing Company.
Permission is granted to reproduce this page for ministry purposes only—not for resale.

Jacob's Ladder

Before Class
- Photocopy reproducible page onto white, heavyweight copy paper. Score all fold lines on ladder **(4A).** Cut out each piece.
- Use an X-Acto knife to cut out areas indicated on ladder.
- Fold all dot lines (mountain) on ladder.
- Fold and crease one sheet of construction paper in half. This is your card.

In Class

- Have children color each piece.
- Follow instructions **Box Stand-Ups** (page 6). See **1.**
- Open card halfway and ladder will stand up. Open card flat and ladder will also be flat.
- Open card flat. Glue angels **(4D)** to ladder. Use only a spot of glue on ladder for each angel.
- Glue rock **(4C)** to card at the foot of ladder, then glue Jacob **(4B)** so his head is on the rock.
- Glue **4E** to outside of card.
- When children open their cards, a ladder pops up.

1

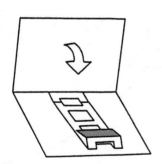

Preschool
Before class, glue bottom tab of ladder to card, and lay it down with top two sections folded back. See **2.** Close card. In class, have children glue top tab. Close card and press. Follow rest of instructions to complete.

2

Materials for one activity
1 sheet construction paper
1 sheet white, heavyweight copy paper
X-Acto knife
scissors
glue stick
crayons

4E

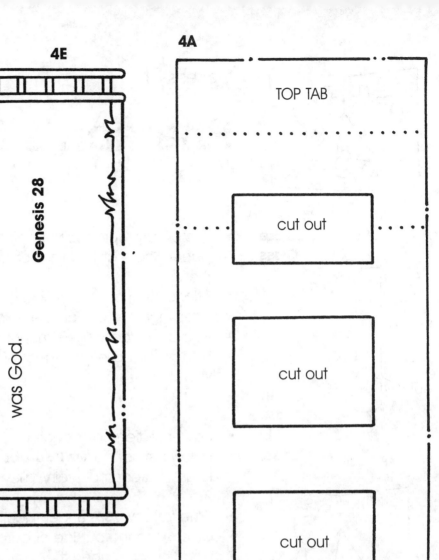

In a dream, Jacob saw angels going up and down a ladder that led to Heaven. Standing above the ladder was God.

Genesis 28

4A

TOP TAB

cut out

cut out

cut out

cut out

BOTTOM TAB

4D

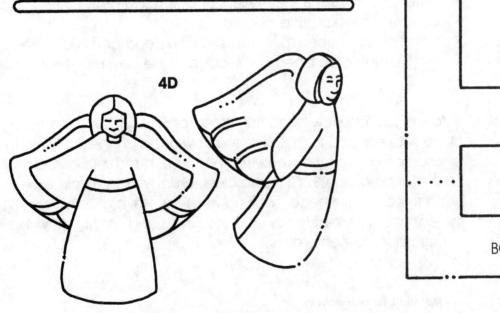

4B

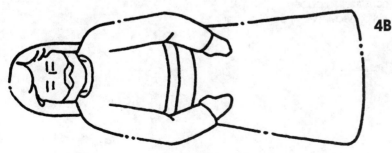

4C

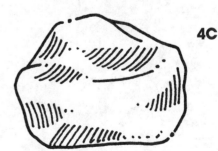

15

© 1996 by The Standard Publishing Company.
Permission is granted to reproduce this page for ministry purposes only—not for resale.

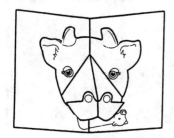

Pharaoh's Dream

1

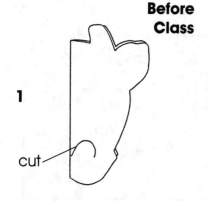

cut

Before Class

- Photocopy reproducible page onto white, heavyweight copy paper. Score all fold lines on cow head **(5A).** Cut out each piece.
- After cutting out the outline of cow head, fold in half, wrong sides together. Cut on the solid line around it's nose. See **1.**
- Fold all dot/dash lines (mountain/valley) on cow head.
- Fold and crease one sheet of construction paper in half. This is your card.

In Class

- Have children color each piece.
- Follow instructions for **Pop-Ups in a Picture** (page 5). Be sure to use correct mountain/valley folds as directed by pattern. See **2.**
- Glue fat cow **(5B)** under mouth of cow head **(5A).**
- Glue **5C** to the outside of card.
- When children open their cards, a cow head pops up. When they flex the card open, it will look as if the cow is chewing.

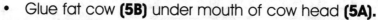

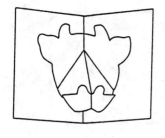

2

Preschool

Before class, fold cow head flat (mountain/valley). Glue the back of the right ear and horn. Place the cow head on the right side of opened card. Align the center at the top of head with center crease of card. See **3.** Close. In class, children can unfold cow head to color. Fold head back up as it was. Have children glue the ear and horn that faces up. Close card and press. Follow rest of instructions to complete.

3

Materials for one activity
1 sheet construction paper
1 sheet white, heavyweight copy paper
scissors
glue stick
crayons

5A

5C

Joseph told Pharaoh
the meaning of his
dreams.

Genesis 41

5B

© 1996 by The Standard Publishing Company.
Permission is granted to reproduce this page for ministry purposes only—not for resale.

Exodus 2

Baby Moses

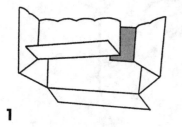

1

Before Class

- Photocopy reproducible page onto white, heavyweight copy paper. Score all fold lines on basket **(6A)** and grass **(6B).** Cut out each piece.
- Fold all dot/dash lines (mountain/valley) on basket and grass.
- Glue the end tab on basket. Bend it around to the under side of the basket edge to secure. See **1.**
- Fold and crease one sheet of blue construction paper in half. This is your card.
- Cut an 8-inch length of yarn.

In Class

- Have children color each piece.
- Glue the bottom of one of the basket tabs and position it on card as shown (one inch from and parallel to center crease of card). See **2.** With basket laying flat, glue other tab. Close card and press.
- Glue tabs on grass and place as shown. See **3.** When blades of grass are bent up, they will stand. Have children draw water waves around the basket.
- Tape one end of yarn to the back of baby Moses **(6C)** and the other end inside basket.
- Glue **6D** to outside of card.
- When children open their cards, the basket stands up straight in the grass in the river.

2

Preschool

Before class, glue one of the bottom tabs of the basket to the card as shown. Fold the basket flat and close card. Follow rest of instructions to complete.

Materials for one activity
1 sheet blue construction paper
1 sheet white, heavyweight copy paper
8-inch length of yarn
tape
scissors
glue stick
crayons

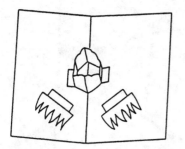

3

6A

TAB

TAB

6C

6B

TAB

TAB

6D

Baby Moses floated in a special basket in the river's tall grass.

Exodus 2

TAB

19

© 1996 by The Standard Publishing Company. Permission is granted to reproduce this page for ministry purposes only—not for resale.

Exodus 3

Burning Bush

Before Class

- Photocopy reproducible page onto white, heavyweight copy paper. Cut out each piece.
- Trace mountain **(7A)** onto brown construction paper folded lengthwise. Align *place on fold* edge of pattern with folded edge of the construction paper. Cut out. Note that the lower part of the folded edge is to be cut where indicated. See **1**.
- Score and fold all dash lines (valley) on mountain.

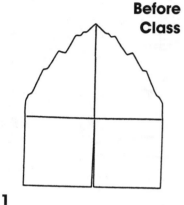

1

In Class

- Have children color each piece.
- Glue shoes **(7B)** and bush **(7C)** to the inside of mountain.
- Fold mountain so that it is standing up and two bottom sections are one on top of the other. See **2**.
- Glue **7D** on bottom section.

Materials for one activity
1 sheet brown construction paper
1 sheet white, heavyweight copy paper
scissors
glue stick
crayons

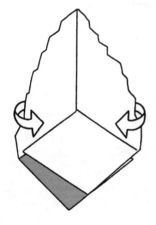

2

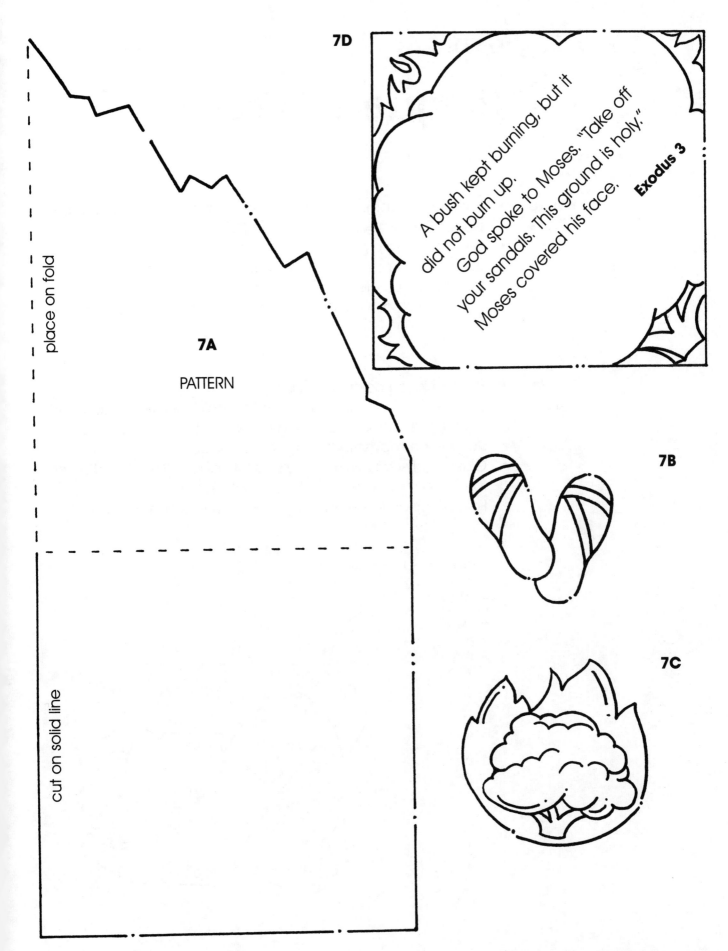

place on fold

7A

PATTERN

cut on solid line

7D

A bush kept burning, but it did not burn up. God spoke to Moses. "Take off your sandals. This ground is holy." Moses covered his face.

Exodus 3

7B

7C

21

© 1996 by The Standard Publishing Company.
Permission is granted to reproduce this page for ministry purposes only—not for resale.

Plague of Frogs

Before Class

- Photocopy reproducible page onto white, heavyweight copy paper. Score all fold lines on frog **(8A).**
- Before cutting out, turn copied paper over and put strips of tape over the area where hand straps meet the frog's body so that the straps will not tear. Cut out each piece.
- Fold all dot/dash lines (mountain/valley) on frog. See illustration.

In Class

- Have children color each piece.
- Teacher can curl the tongue **(8B)** by holding the wide end of the tongue shape and pulling a scissor blade along the underside in one movement. Tongue will curl up.
- Glue wiggly eyes on the frog's head. Tape the wide end of the tongue on the underside of the frog's mouth.
- Fold straps on each side of frog to fit child's hand. Staple.

Materials for one activity
1 sheet white, heavyweight copy paper
2 wiggly eyes
tape
stapler
scissors
glue stick
crayons

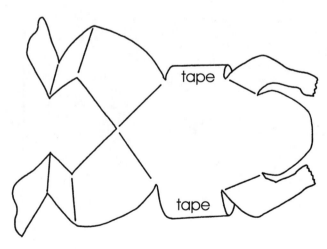

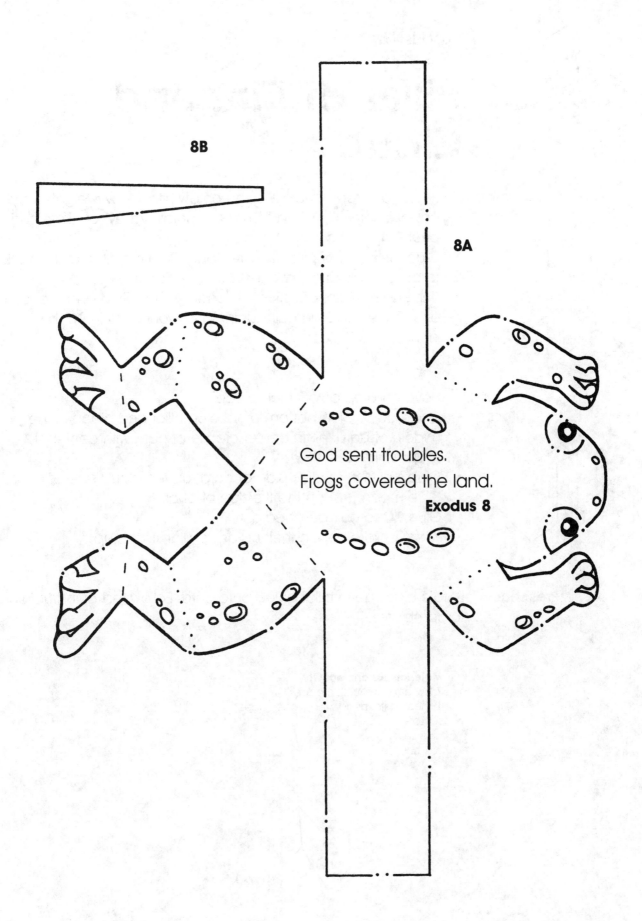

8B

8A

God sent troubles.
Frogs covered the land.
Exodus 8

23

© 1996 by The Standard Publishing Company.
Permission is granted to reproduce this page for ministry purposes only—not for resale.

Pillar of Fire and Cloud

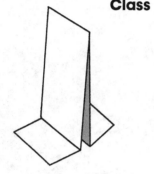

1

Before Class

- Photocopy reproducible page onto white, heavyweight copy paper. Score all dot/dash lines (mountain/valley) on fire/cloud pillar **(9A).** Cut out each piece.
- Glue the back of pillar (not the tabs). Fold cloud and fire back to back, making an inverted **T**-shape. See **1.**
- Cut one sheet of construction paper in half. Fold and crease one of the halves in half again. This is your card (4 1/2-by-6-inches).

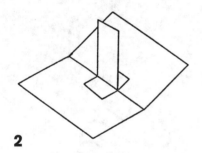

2

In Class

- Have children color each piece.
- Open card. Glue bottom of tabs on pillar and place in the middle of card. Align center crease of card with center of **T**-shape pillar. See **2.**
- Glue sun **(9B)** to the inside of card, on the cloud side of pillar. Glue moon **(9B)** on the fire side of pillar.
- Glue **9C** to outside of card.
- When children open their cards, a pillar stands up.

Preschool

Before class, have pillar glued onto card. Follow rest of instructions to complete.

Materials for one activity
1/2 sheet construction paper
1 sheet white, heavyweight copy paper
scissors
glue stick
crayons

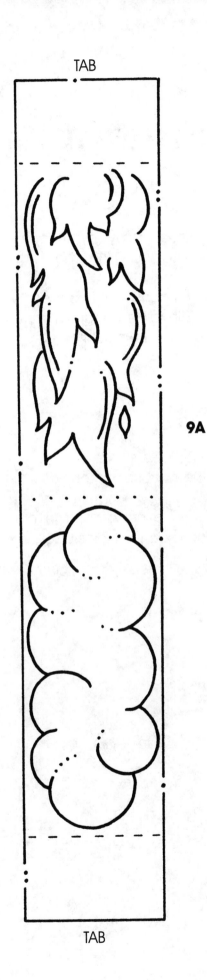

TAB

9A

TAB

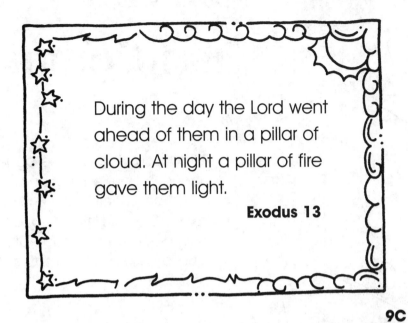

During the day the Lord went ahead of them in a pillar of cloud. At night a pillar of fire gave them light.

Exodus 13

9C

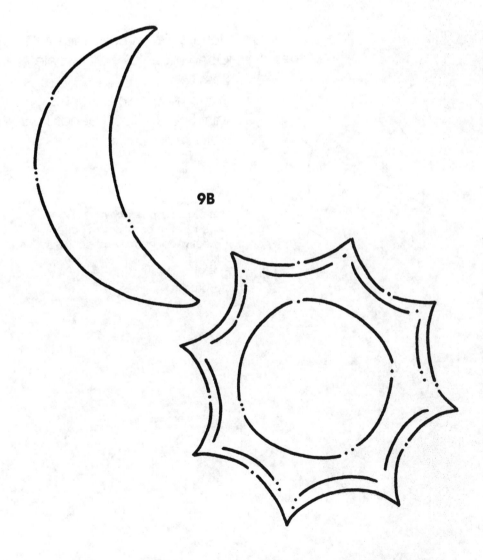

9B

25

© 1996 by The Standard Publishing Company.
Permission is granted to reproduce this page for ministry purposes only—not for resale.

Ten Commandments

Before Class

- Photocopy reproducible page onto white, heavyweight copy paper. Cut out each piece. Cut slits on cloud **(10B)** where indicated on pattern.
- Trace Mt. Sinai **(10A)** onto folded brown construction paper. Align *place on fold* edge of pattern with folded edge of construction paper. Cut out. Cut slits on Mt. Sinai where indicated on pattern.

1

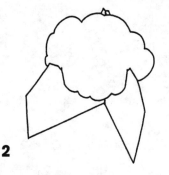

In Class

- Have children color tablets **(10C)** to look like stone.
- Open mountain. Glue tablets near the bottom of mountain. See **1.**
- Stand mountain upright. Slide slits on cloud into slits on mountain. See **2.** Cloud bends forward and mountain folds backward (valley).

2

Materials for one activity
1 sheet brown construction paper
1 sheet white, heavyweight copy paper
scissors
glue stick
crayons

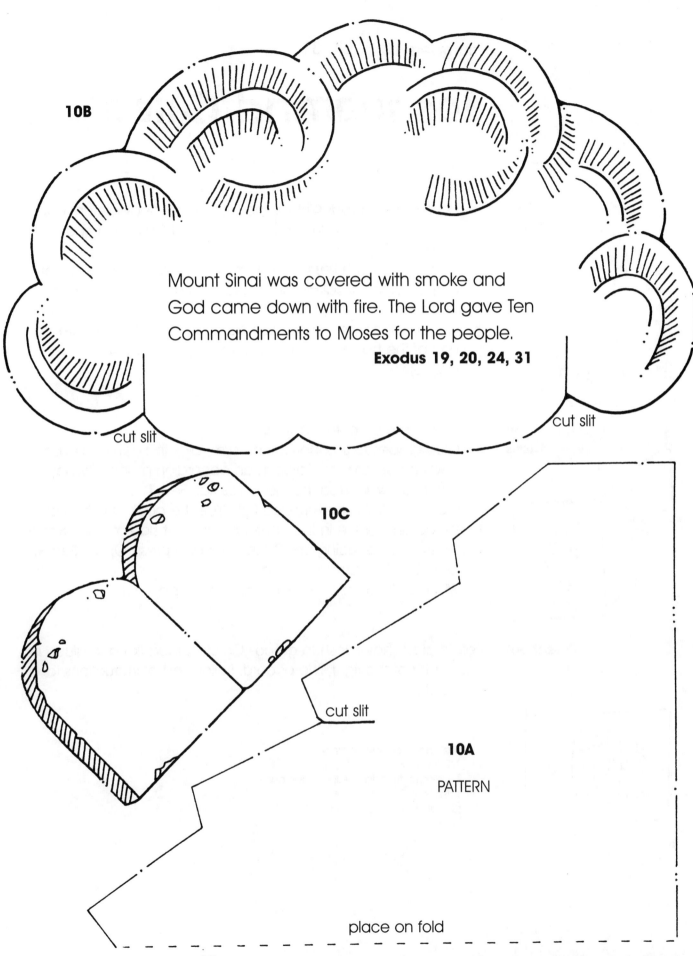

10B

Mount Sinai was covered with smoke and God came down with fire. The Lord gave Ten Commandments to Moses for the people.

Exodus 19, 20, 24, 31

cut slit

cut slit

10C

cut slit

10A

PATTERN

place on fold

27

© 1996 by The Standard Publishing Company.
Permission is granted to reproduce this page for ministry purposes only—not for resale.

Joshua and Caleb

1

Before Class

- Photocopy reproducible page onto white, heavyweight copy paper. Score all fold lines on Joshua and Caleb **(11A)** and grapes **(11B).** Cut out each piece.
- Fold all dot/dash lines (mountain/valley) on Joshua/Caleb and grapes. Joshua/Caleb will be folded in an accordion manner when flat.
- Cut one sheet of construction paper in half. Fold and crease one of the halves in half again. This is your card (4 1/2-by-6-inches).

In Class

- Have children color each piece.
- Glue grapes to Joshua/Caleb's arm, aligning center creases. Fold Joshua-grapes-Caleb in an accordion manner (valley, mountain, valley) so the piece lies flat. See **1.**
- Open card. While still folded flat, glue the back of right man shape and place in the center of the right side of card. See **2.** Glue the side facing up. Close card and press. Open. See **3.**
- Glue **11C** to outside of card.
- When children open their cards, grapes pop out.

2

Preschool

Before class, have Joshua-grapes-Caleb folded flat and glued in the center of the right side of card. Follow rest of instructions to complete.

3

Materials for one activity
1/2 sheet construction paper
1 sheet white, heavyweight copy paper
scissors
glue stick
crayons

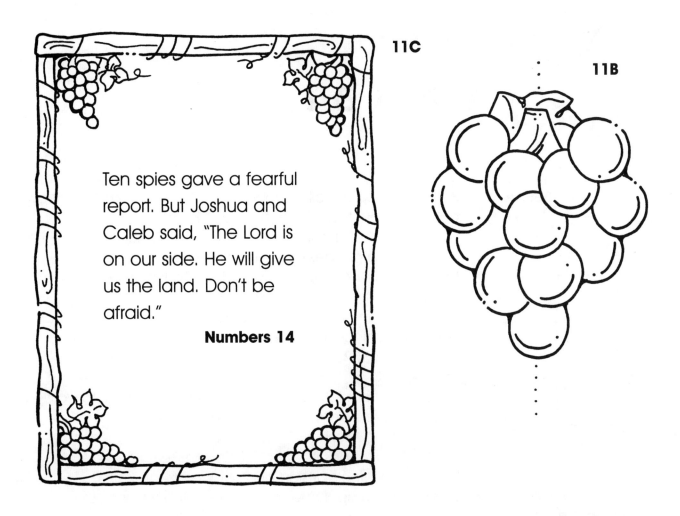

11C

Ten spies gave a fearful report. But Joshua and Caleb said, "The Lord is on our side. He will give us the land. Don't be afraid."

Numbers 14

11B

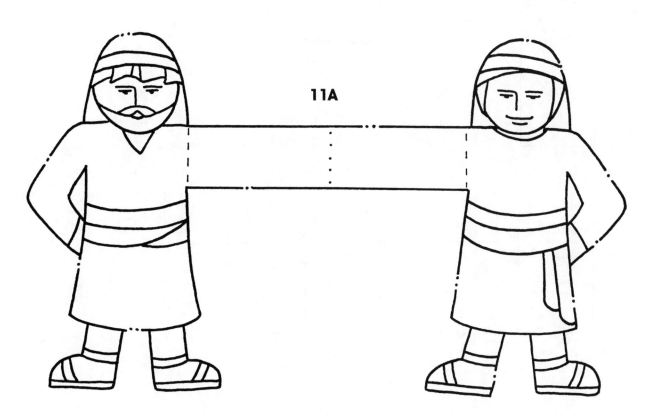

11A

© 1996 by The Standard Publishing Company.
Permission is granted to reproduce this page for ministry purposes only—not for resale.

Joshua 6

Walls of Jericho

Before Class

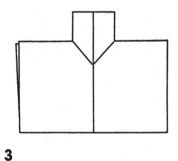

1

- Photocopy reproducible page onto white, heavyweight copy paper. Cut out the outline of card **(12).**
- Fold card in half, lengthwise, right sides together. See **1.** The + in the middle of card indicates a cross fold.
- Fold the top extension (trumpet) down so that it lies below the top edge of the card. Crease fold. See **2.**
- Open card and bring bottom edge up to top edge, wrong sides together (copied card showing on front and back). Crease. See **3.** Put a dot of glue inside card to keep it together.
- Close card from left to right, pulling trumpet (**V**-fold) forward to inside of card. See **4.**

In Class

2

- Have children color inside and outside of card.
- When children open their cards, the trumpet pops out.

Materials for one activity
1 sheet white, heavyweight copy paper
scissors
glue stick
crayons

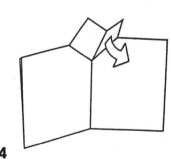

3

4

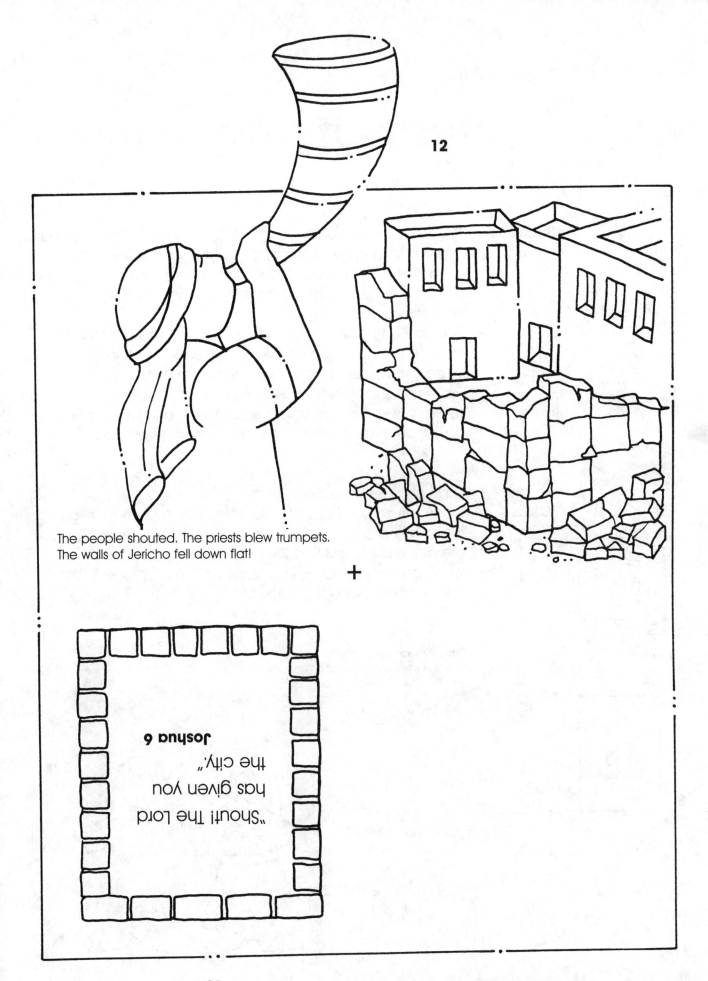

The people shouted. The priests blew trumpets.
The walls of Jericho fell down flat!

+

"Shout! The Lord
has given you
the city."
Joshua 6

31

© 1996 by The Standard Publishing Company.
Permission is granted to reproduce this page for ministry purposes only—not for resale.

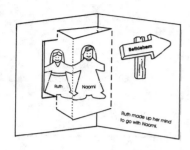

Ruth and Naomi

Before Class

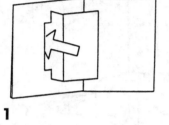

1

- Photocopy reproducible page and pattern **13B** from this page onto white, heavyweight copy paper. Score all fold lines on card **(13A)** and women **(13B).** Cut out each piece.
- Use an X-Acto knife to cut out the rectangle and the slits along solid lines on card.
- Fold top edge down to bottom edge, wrong sides together (copied card showing on front and back). The + in the middle of card indicates a cross fold. Crease fold. See **1.**
- Easing card closed from left to right, bring inside center section forward. See **1.** Close and crease. The flap from the inside will now show through and lie flat on the outside of card.

In Class

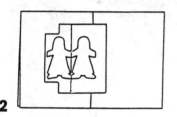

2

- Have children color each piece.
- Open card. Glue Ruth and Naomi to the inside flap, aligning the center crease on the figures with the flap crease line. (Both are mountain folds.) See **2.**
- When card is closed, Ruth is alone on the front. See **3.** When card is open, Ruth joins Naomi.

Materials for one activity
2 sheets white, heavyweight copy paper
X-Acto knife
scissors
glue stick
crayons

3

13B

Ruth   Naomi

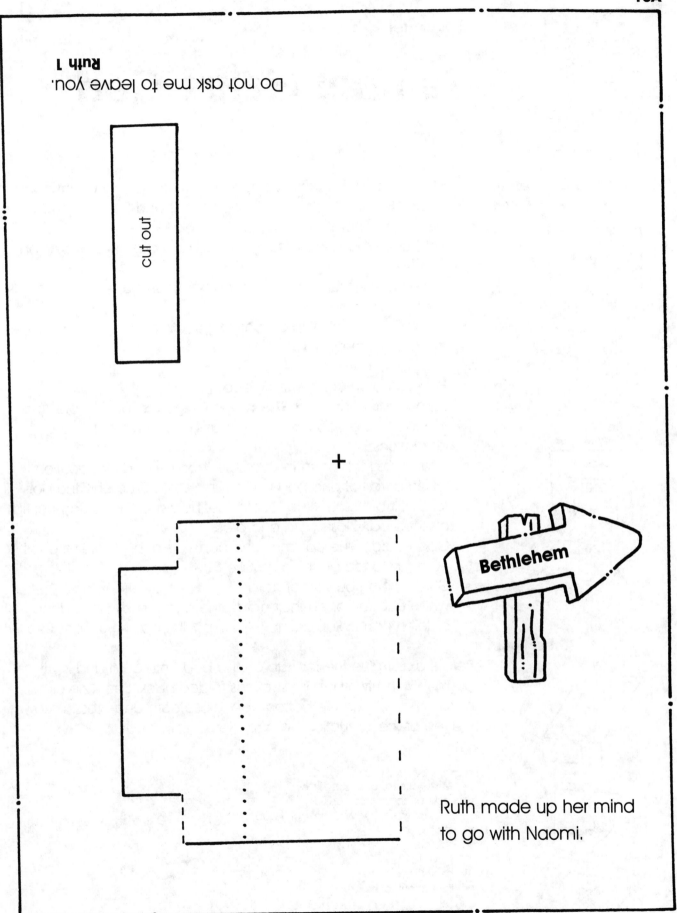

Do not ask me to leave you.
Ruth 1

cut out

Bethlehem

Ruth made up her mind
to go with Naomi.

33

© 1996 by The Standard Publishing Company.
Permission is granted to reproduce this page for ministry purposes only—not for resale.

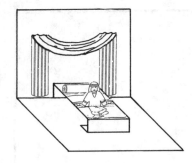

1 Samuel 2, 3

Samuel Hears God

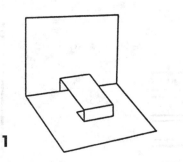

1

Before Class

- Photocopy reproducible page onto white, heavyweight copy paper. Score all fold lines on bed **(14A)** and Samuel **(14B).** Cut out each piece.
- Fold all dot lines (mountain) on bed and dash line (valley) on Samuel.
- Fold and crease one sheet of construction paper in half. This is your card.
- Cut a 2-by-8-inch strip of lightweight fabric for a swag between the two columns **(14C).**

In Class

- Have children color each piece.
- Follow instructions **Box Stand-Ups** (page 6). See **1.** Note: The top tab of the bed is referred to as a bottom tab in those instructions.
- After gluing tabs, turn the card so that the bed is in position. Open card flat and bed will lie flat. See **1.** Glue only the bottom half of Samuel (up to fold line, his waist). Place Samuel flat on the bed. Close card and press.
- Open card. Glue columns on each side of bed. Staple ends of fabric to top of columns. See **2.**
- Glue **14D** on outside of card.
- When children open their cards, the bed stands up and the children can sit Samuel up. His arms will keep him upright. See **3.**

2

Preschool

3

Before class, glue the top tab on the bed onto card and lay it down with the two bottom sections folded back. See **4.** In class, have children glue the bottom tab, close card and press. Follow the rest of the instructions to complete.

4

Materials for one activity
1 sheet construction paper
1 sheet white, heavyweight copy paper
stapler
scissors
glue stick
crayons
lightweight fabric

34

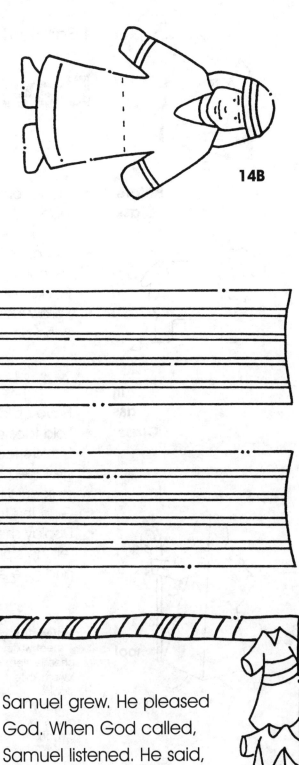

14B

14C

14A

TOP TAB

BOTTOM TAB

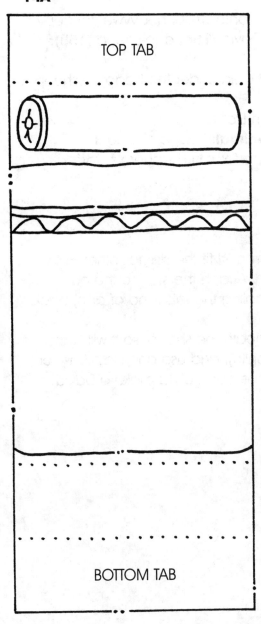

14D

Samuel grew. He pleased God. When God called, Samuel listened. He said, "Speak, Lord. I am your servant, and I am listening."

1 Samuel 2, 3

© 1996 by The Standard Publishing Company.
Permission is granted to reproduce this page for ministry purposes only—not for resale.

1 Samuel 16

David the Shepherd

Before Class

- Photocopy reproducible page onto white, heavyweight copy paper. Score all fold lines on David **(15A)** and sheep **(15B)**. Cut out each piece.
- Use an X-Acto knife to cut out area under the head on sheep as indicated.
- Fold all dot lines (mountain) on David.
- Follow instructions **Stand-Up Animals** (page 6). See **1.**
- Bend an 8-inch chenille stem to form a shepherd's staff.

1

In Class

- Have children color David.
- Fold tabs on David behind him and fit the slits together. Fold David's feet to the front of him. Attach the staff to the out-stretched arm, folding and stapling the tab (end of arm) back to secure it. See **2.**
- Glue the tabs together underneath the sheep, so it will stand.
- Display sheep (one for each child), and use one David as you tell the story. After the story, have each child make a David and give each child a sheep.

2

Materials for one activity
1 sheet white, heavyweight copy paper
chenille stem, cut to 8-inch length
X-Acto knife
stapler
scissors
glue stick
crayons

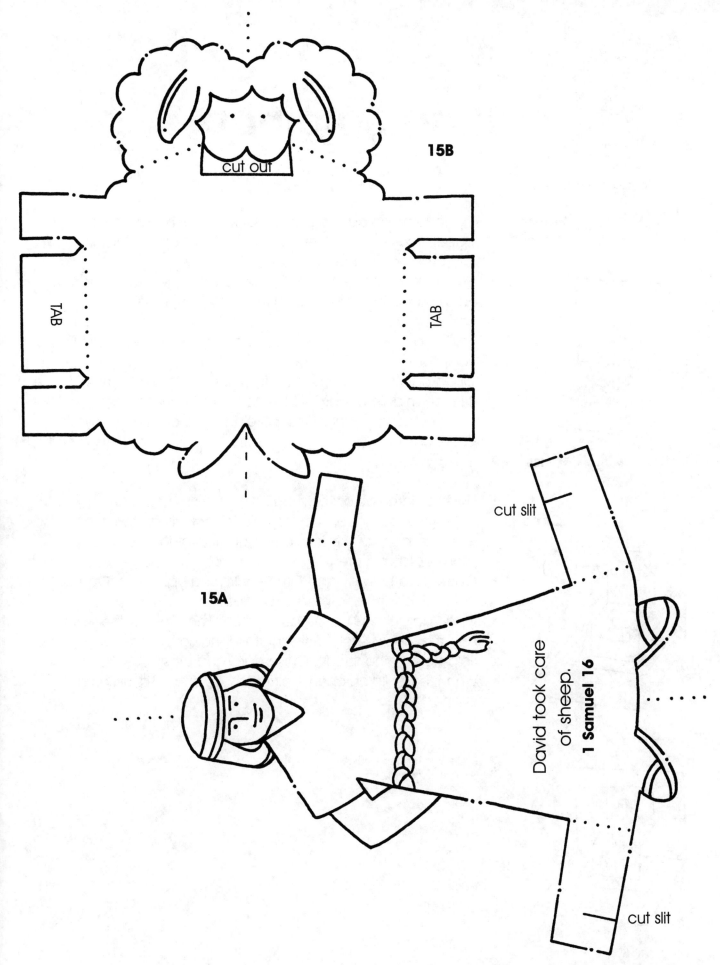

15B

cut out

TAB

TAB

cut slit

15A

David took care of sheep.
1 Samuel 16

cut slit

37

© 1996 by The Standard Publishing Company.
Permission is granted to reproduce this page for ministry purposes only—not for resale.

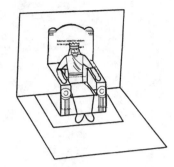

King Solomon

Before Class

1

- Photocopy reproducible page onto white, heavyweight copy paper. Score all fold lines on throne **(16A)** and Solomon **(16B)**. Cut out each piece.
- Use an X-Acto knife to cut slits along solid lines on throne.
- Fold all dot/dash lines (mountain/valley) on throne and Solomon.
- Fold and crease one sheet of construction paper in half. This is your card.
- Open card. Glue the back side of the bottom tab **(16A)**. Place it in the middle of card. Align the bottom tab back edge with center crease of card. See **1.** Fold throne down so it lays flat. Close card.

In Class

2

- Have children color Solomon.
- Lay throne out flat and color. Fold it back up as it was.
- Glue the back of the tab facing up (top of throne). See **1.** Close card and press.
- Open card halfway and throne will stand up. See **2.** Open card flat and throne will also be flat.
- Open card flat. Glue the back of Solomon, below the waist and the elbow. Align all the corresponding fold lines and place Solomon on the throne. Close card and press.
- When the children open their cards, Solomon sits up on his throne. See **3.**

Materials for one activity
1 sheet construction paper
1 sheet white, heavyweight copy paper
X-Acto knife
scissors
glue stick
crayons

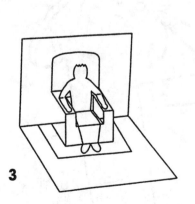

3

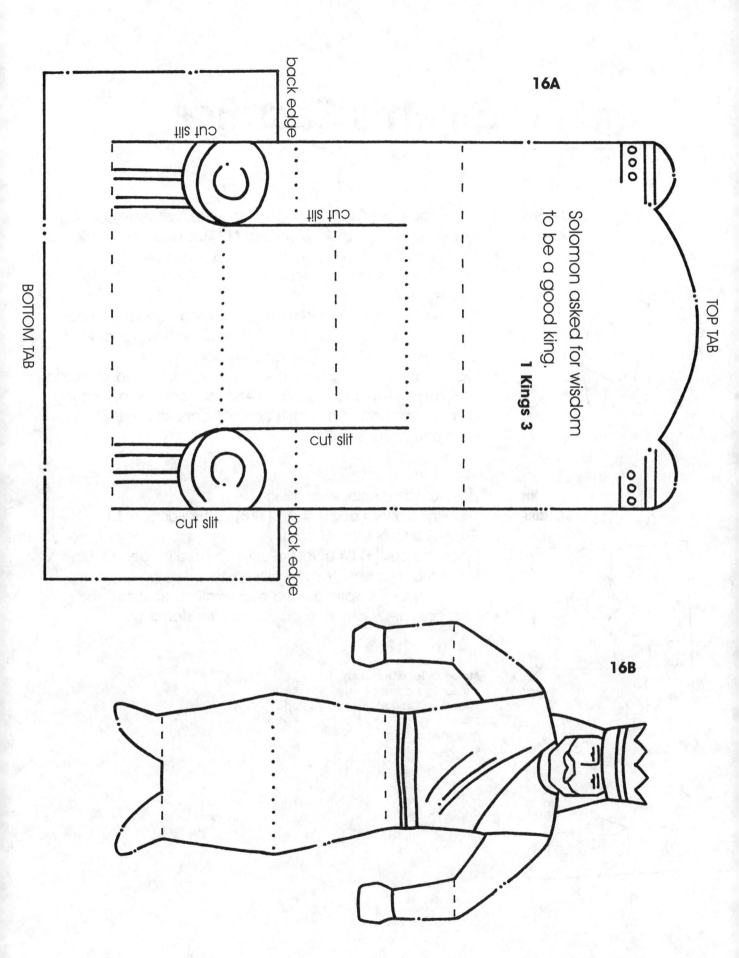

16A

back edge

cut slit

cut slit

cut slit

cut slit

cut slit

back edge

BOTTOM TAB

TOP TAB

Solomon asked for wisdom
to be a good king.
1 Kings 3

16B

© 1996 by The Standard Publishing Company.
Permission is granted to reproduce this page for ministry purposes only—not for resale.

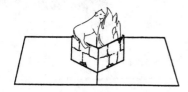

Elijah's Sacrifice

Before Class

- Photocopy reproducible page onto white, heavyweight copy paper. Score all fold lines on altar **(17A).** Cut out each piece.
- Fold all dot/dash lines (mountain/valley) on altar.
- Fold altar to make an open-ended box. Glue end tab to secure. See **1.**
- Fold and crease one sheet of light-colored construction paper in half. This is your card. (The children will color water around altar. If you use dark paper, coloring won't show.)
- Open card. Glue the backside of the two bottom tabs on altar. With altar opened to a square, press tabs onto card, aligning diagonal corners of altar with center crease of card. Close card and press. See **2.**

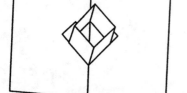

1

In Class

- Have children color each piece.
- Glue the bottom edge of fire **(17B)** onto altar. See **3.**
- Glue **17D** to outside of card.
- Place the bull **(17C)** across altar when card is opened. Slip it inside the altar when card is closed.
- Color a ditch of water around altar and flames in the water.
- When children open their cards, the altar stands up.

Materials for one activity
1 sheet light-colored construction paper
1 sheet white, heavyweight copy paper
scissors
glue stick
crayons

2

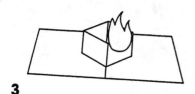

3

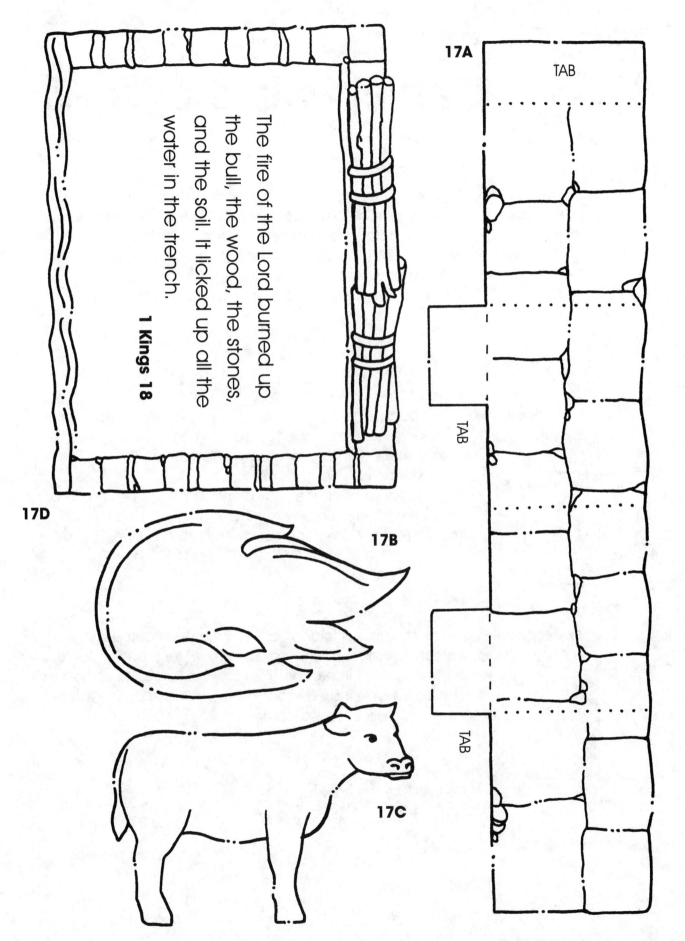

17A

TAB

TAB

TAB

The fire of the Lord burned up the bull, the wood, the stones, and the soil. It licked up all the water in the trench.

1 Kings 18

17D

17B

17C

41

© 1996 by The Standard Publishing Company.
Permission is granted to reproduce this page for ministry purposes only—not for resale.

Daniel and the Lions

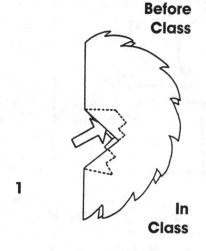

1

Before Class

- Photocopy reproducible page onto white, heavyweight copy paper. Score all fold lines on lion **(18A).** Cut out each piece.
- Use an X-Acto knife to cut the zig-zag slit at lion's mouth.
- Fold lion down center, right sides together. Open. Gently pull the jaws forward to form two **V**-folds. Fold lion flat. See **1.** Dotted lines show position of jaws folded inside.

In Class

- Have children color each piece.
- Open card. Glue the back of lion head, being careful not to get glue around the mouth. Place lion on card, aligning center crease of lion with center crease of card. See **2.**
- Glue **18B** on outside of card.
- When children open their cards, the mouth of the lion will pop open. Have the children press the jaws in to close the lion's mouth. Flex the card open so the mouth can open again.

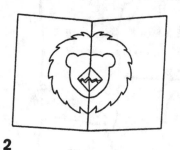

2

Preschool

Before class, with lion folded flat, glue the back of the right side and place it on right side of card. Align center creases. See **3.** Close. In class, children can color lion. Fold lion back up as it was. Have children glue the side facing up and close card. Press. Follow rest of instructions to complete.

3

Materials for one activity
1 sheet construction paper
1 sheet white, heavyweight copy paper
X-Acto knife
scissors
glue stick
crayons

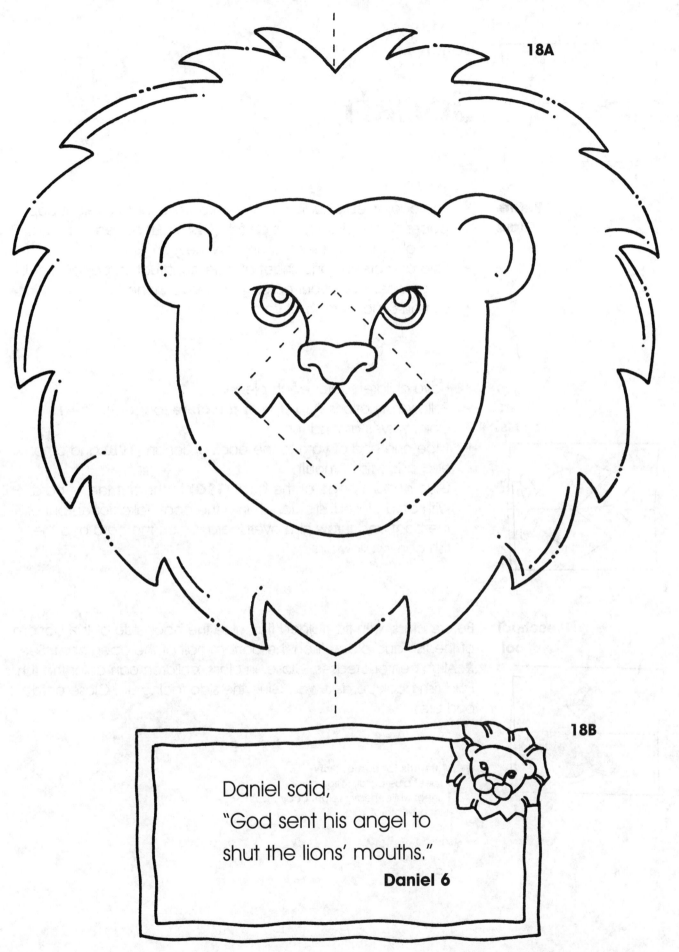

18A

18B

Daniel said,
"God sent his angel to
shut the lions' mouths."

Daniel 6

 © 1996 by The Standard Publishing Company.
Permission is granted to reproduce this page for ministry purposes only—not for resale.

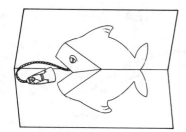

Jonah

Before Class
- Photocopy reproducible page onto white, heavyweight copy paper. Score all fold lines on fish **(19A).** Cut out each piece.
- Fold all dot/dash lines (mountain/valley) on fish.
- Fold and crease one sheet of blue construction paper in half lengthwise. This is your card (4 1/2-by-12-inches).
- Cut an 8-inch length of yarn.

In Class
- Have children color each piece.
- Follow instructions **Pop-Ups in a Picture** (page 5). See **1.**
- Color waves around fish.
- Tape one end of yarn to the back of Jonah **(19B)** and other end inside fish's mouth.
- Glue bottom edge of the boat **(19C)** to the outside of card.
- With card closed, slip Jonah into the boat. Take Jonah out of the boat and throw him overboard. Open the card and the fish can swallow him.

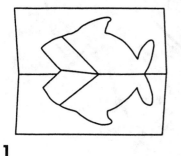

1

Preschool

Before class, with fish folded flat, glue the back side of the bottom of the fish and place it on the bottom half of the open card. See **2.** Align center creases. Close. In class, children can color the fish. Fold fish back up as it was. Glue the side facing up. Close card and press.

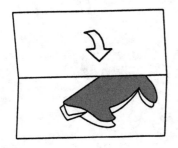

2

Materials for one activity
1 sheet blue construction paper
1 sheet white, heavyweight copy paper
8-inch length of yarn
tape
scissors
glue stick
crayons

19A

19B

19C

Sailors threw Jonah into the sea.
Jonah stayed three days and nights
in the fish God had prepared.

Jonah 1

45

© 1996 by The Standard Publishing Company.
Permission is granted to reproduce this page for ministry purposes only—not for resale.

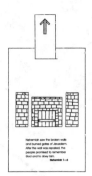

Rebuild the Walls

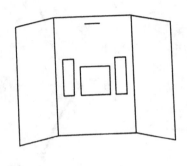

1

Before Class

- Photocopy **20A** and **20B** onto white, heavyweight copy paper. Cut out both on outlines.
- To make the card, score one sheet of heavyweight copy paper 2 3/4 inches from each side edge. Fold each side in and edges will meet in the middle. Seam will be the back of the card. Card will be a 5 1/2-by-8 1/2-inch rectangle.
- Glue back of **20A** and place on front of card. Bottom edge of **20A** must be aligned with bottom edge of card.
- Open card flat. Use an X-Acto knife to cut out the three sections, and slit on **20A** where indicated. Make sure to cut only the front of the card. Do not cut holes through the back of the card. See **1**.
- Turn card over and glue-stick 1/4 inch along inside bottom edge of card. Press the two sides down to seal bottom edge. Tape seam down back of card. See **2**.
- Glue back of wall insert **(20B)** and place on poster paper. Cut out.

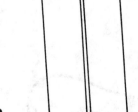

2

In Class

- Have children color wall insert.
- Place the wall insert into the card, right sides up. Slip the pull tab (arrow) into the slit on the card. (The word *cut* will be covered by the pull tab.) See **3**.
- Put a spot of glue at the top inside edge of card to close top. Don't get glue on pull tab.
- When tab is pushed down, walls appear broken. When tab is pulled up, walls are repaired.

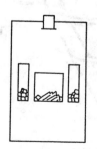

3

Materials for one activity
3 sheets white, heavyweight copy paper
poster board, 9-by-6-inches
X-Acto knife
tape
scissors
glue stick
crayons

cut

cut out

cut out

cut out

Nehemiah saw the broken walls
and burned gates of Jerusalem.
After the wall was repaired, the
people promised to remember
God and to obey him.

Nehemiah 1—6

align with bottom edge of card

© 1996 by The Standard Publishing Company.
Permission is granted to reproduce this page for ministry purposes only—not for resale.

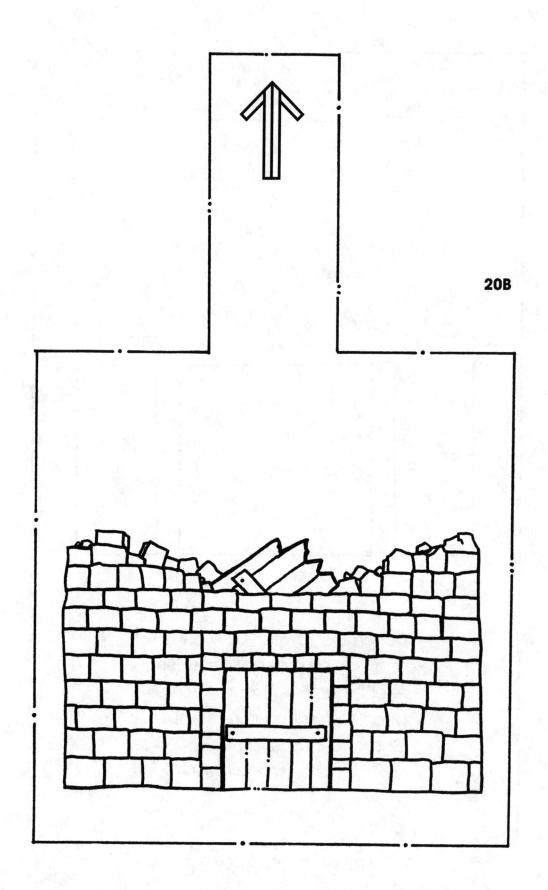

20B

© 1996 by The Standard Publishing Company.
Permission is granted to reproduce this page for ministry purposes only—not for resale.

Luke 1

Angel Talks to Mary

Before Class

- Photocopy reproducible page onto white, heavyweight copy paper. Score all fold lines on angel **(21B)** and Mary **(21C)**. Cut out each piece.
- Cut two sheets of construction paper to 7-by-9-inches. Fold and crease both papers in half lengthwise, making cards 3 1/2-by-9-inches. One of the cards will be the background, the other will be the foreground. Score 1/2-inch tabs along the long edges of the foreground and fold back (mountain). See **1**.
- Place stencil **(21A)** onto the foreground (paper with folded tabs), aligning center creases. Using **21A** as a stencil, trace around it. Use an X-Acto knife to cut out the area on the foreground. See **2**.

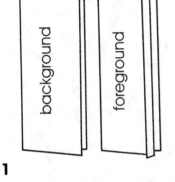

1

In Class

- Have children color each piece.
- Glue the back of the angel (except wing) and match the angel edge with the right edge of the cut out section on the foreground.
- Glue the back of Mary and place on the background, aligning center folds.
- Slip the foreground into the background with the tabs on the outside. Have children glue each long tab and press onto the background. See **3**.
- Glue **21D** onto the outside of the card.

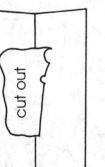

2

Materials for one activity
2 sheets of construction paper trimmed to 7-by-9-inches
1 sheet white, heavyweight copy paper
X-Acto knife
scissors
glue stick
crayons

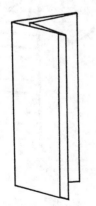

3

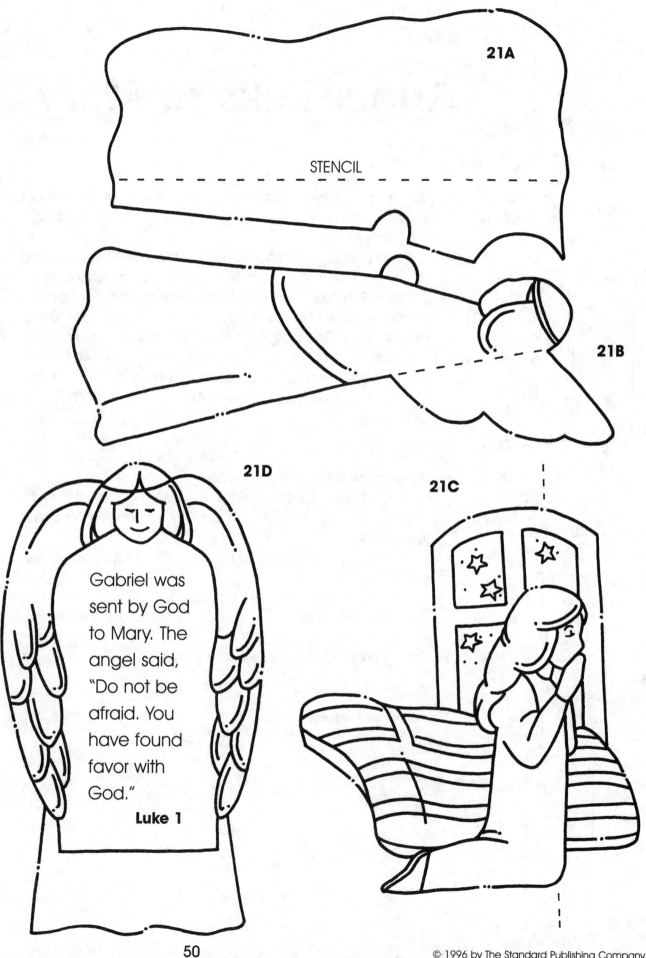

21A

STENCIL

21B

21D

21C

Gabriel was sent by God to Mary. The angel said, "Do not be afraid. You have found favor with God."

Luke 1

50

© 1996 by The Standard Publishing Company.
Permission is granted to reproduce this page for ministry purposes only—not for resale.

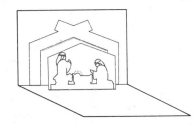

Baby Jesus

Before Class

1

- Photocopy reproducible page and the box support **(22A)** from this page onto white, heavyweight copy paper. Cut out each piece.
- Glue manger scene **(22C)** onto construction paper for stability. Cut out.
- Fold and crease one sheet of construction paper in half. This is your card.
- Follow instructions **Box Support** (page 7). See **1.**

In Class

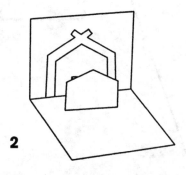

2

- Have children color each piece.
- Open card. Glue the back of stable **(22B)** and place on card, aligning bottom edge of stable with center crease of card.
- Follow instructions for **Box Support** (page 7). Glue manger scene onto support. See **2.**
- Glue manger **(22D)** to outside of card.
- When children open their cards halfway, manger scene stands up.

Materials for one activity
1 sheet construction paper
2 sheets white, heavyweight copy paper
scrap of construction paper
scissors
glue stick
crayons

22A

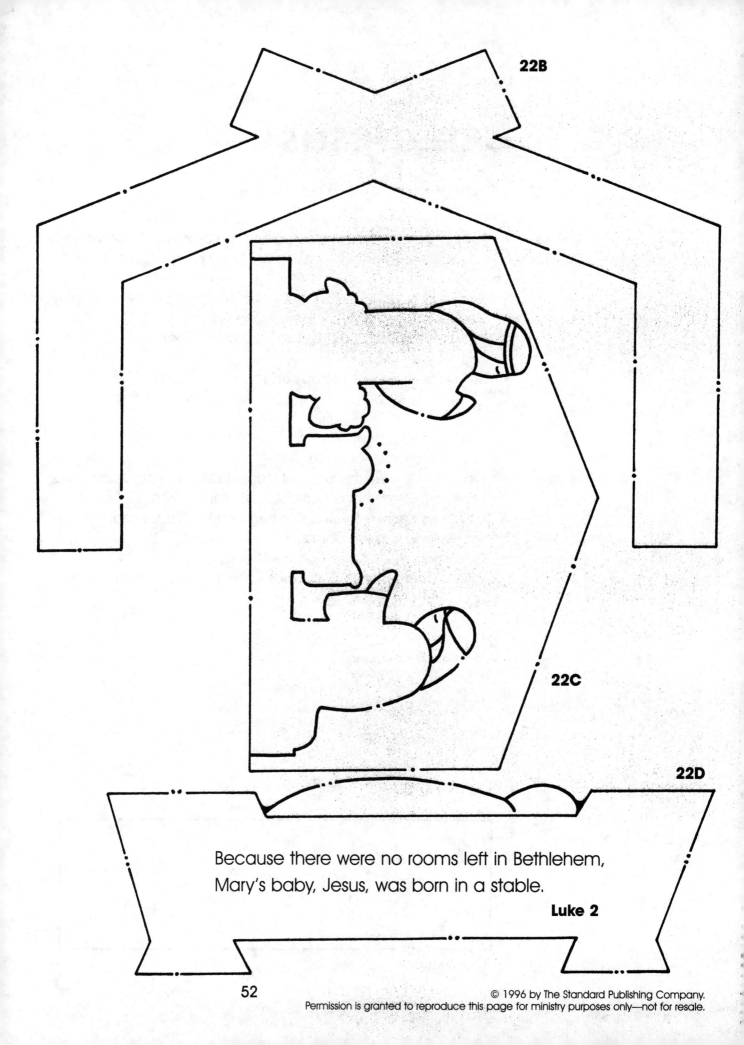

22B

22C

22D

Because there were no rooms left in Bethlehem,
Mary's baby, Jesus, was born in a stable.

Luke 2

© 1996 by The Standard Publishing Company.
Permission is granted to reproduce this page for ministry purposes only—not for resale.

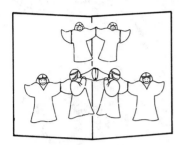

Luke 2

Good News

Before Class
- Photocopy reproducible page onto white, heavyweight copy paper. Score all fold lines on four-angel strip **(23A)** and angel pair **(23B).** Cut out each piece.
- Fold all dot/dash lines (mountain/valley) on angels. They will be folded in an accordion manner and lie flat (valley, mountain, valley).
- Fold and crease one sheet of blue construction paper in half. This is your card.

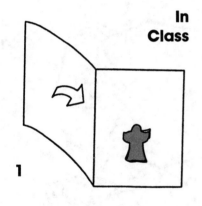

In Class
- Have the children color each piece.
- Open card. Glue the back of the right side of four-angel strip and place in the center of the right side of card. Glue back of angel facing up. Close card and press. See **1.**
- Glue backside of both wing tips of angel pair and place above other angels. Align center creases of angel pair and card. See **2.**
- Have children add foil sticker stars all around the angels.
- Glue **23C** to outside of card.
- When children open their cards, the angels pop out.

1

Preschool

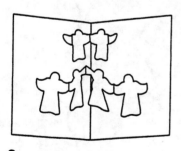

Before class, have four-angel strip folded flat, in accordion manner, and glued in the center of the right side of card. See **1.** Glue angel pair on card as directed. In class, the children can open the card and lay the four-angel strip out flat to color. Fold the strip back up in accordion manner. Glue the back of the four-angel strip facing up. Close card and press. Follow rest of instructions to complete.

2

Materials for one activity
1 sheet blue construction paper
1 sheet white, heavyweight copy paper
foil star stickers, 10-15
scissors
glue stick
crayons

23B

23A

23C

The angels praised God saying, "Glory to God. Peace to his people on earth."

Luke 2

54

© 1996 by The Standard Publishing Company.
Permission is granted to reproduce this page for ministry purposes only—not for resale.

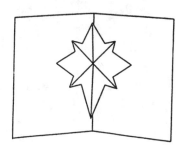

Matthew 2

Wise Men

Before Class
- Photocopy reproducible page onto white, heavyweight copy paper. Score all fold lines on star **(24A).** Cut out each piece.
- Fold all dot/dash lines (mountain/valley) on star. See **1.**
- Fold and crease one sheet of blue construction paper in half. This is your card.

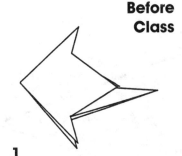

1

In Class
- Have children color each piece.
- Follow instructions **Pop-Ups in a Picture** (page 5). See **2.** The top and bottom points of the star are not glued; they are **V**-folds.
- Glue **24B** to outside of card. Optional: Add star stickers to inside and outside of card.
- When children open their cards, the star pops out.

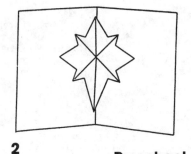

2

Preschool

Before class, have star folded flat, and glued in the center of the right side of card. See **3.** Align the center point of star with center crease of card. Close. In class, the children can open card and lay star out flat to color. Fold star back up as it was. Have children glue the side facing up. Close card and press. Follow rest of instructions to complete.

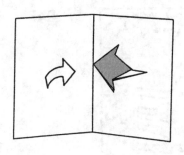

3

Materials for one activity
1 sheet blue construction paper
1 sheet white, heavyweight copy paper
scissors
glue stick
crayons
star stickers (optional)

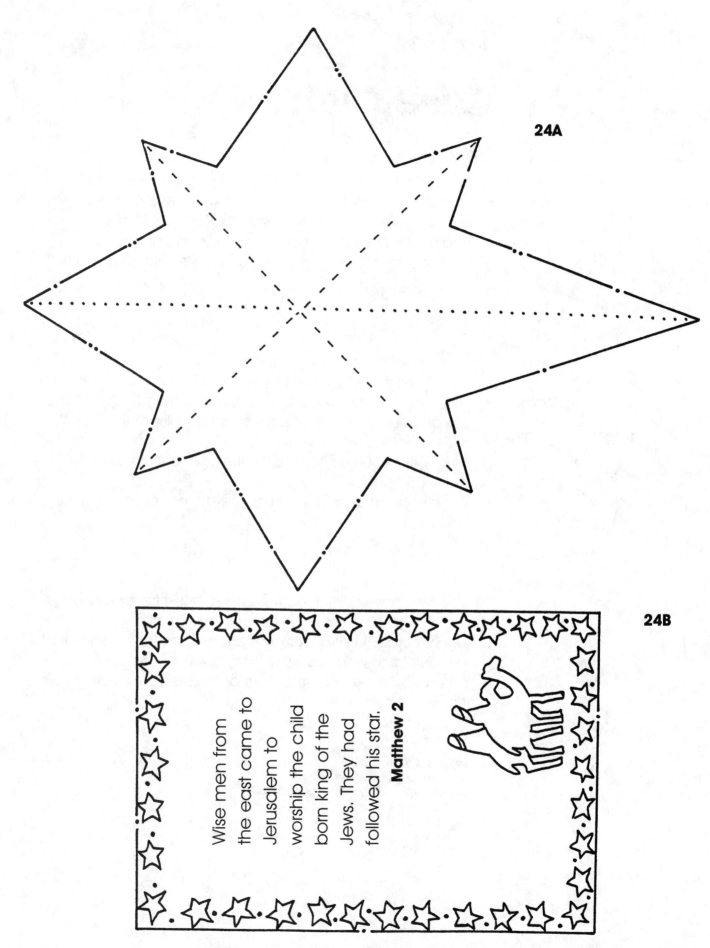

24A

24B

Wise men from
the east came to
Jerusalem to
worship the child
born king of the
Jews. They had
followed his star.

Matthew 2

© 1996 by The Standard Publishing Company.
Permission is granted to reproduce this page for ministry purposes only—not for resale.

Young Jesus in the Temple

Before Class

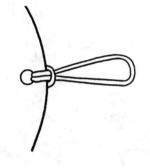

1

- Photocopy reproducible page onto white, heavyweight copy paper. Staying 1/2 inch beyond outline, cut out **25A** and **25B**. Cut out **25C** along outline.
- Using **25C** as a pattern, trace and cut one circle from poster board.
- Glue the back of **25A** and place on the poster board. Punch holes.
- Punch holes on **25B**.
- Turn circle over. Glue the back of **25B**. Align the two holes at the edges and the single and double notches and position on poster board. Cut off paper that extends beyond poster board. The circle will have one side right side up, and other side will be upside down.
- Loop a medium size rubber band through each punched hole. See **1**.

In Class

- Have children color both sides of the circle.
- Have children hold a circle in front of them. Have Jesus appear right side up. Loop thumbs through rubber bands and turn the circle over and over, until the rubber bands are tight on thumbs. Release the circle and slightly flex rubber bands (pull hands apart). Jesus appears to be seated between temple pillars. See **2**.

Materials for one activity
1 sheet white, heavyweight copy paper
poster board approximately 4-inches square
hole punch
2 rubber bands
scissors
glue stick
crayons

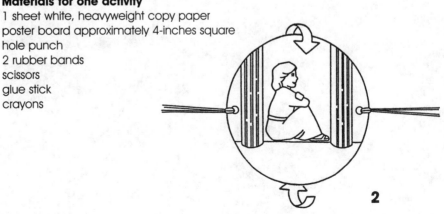

2

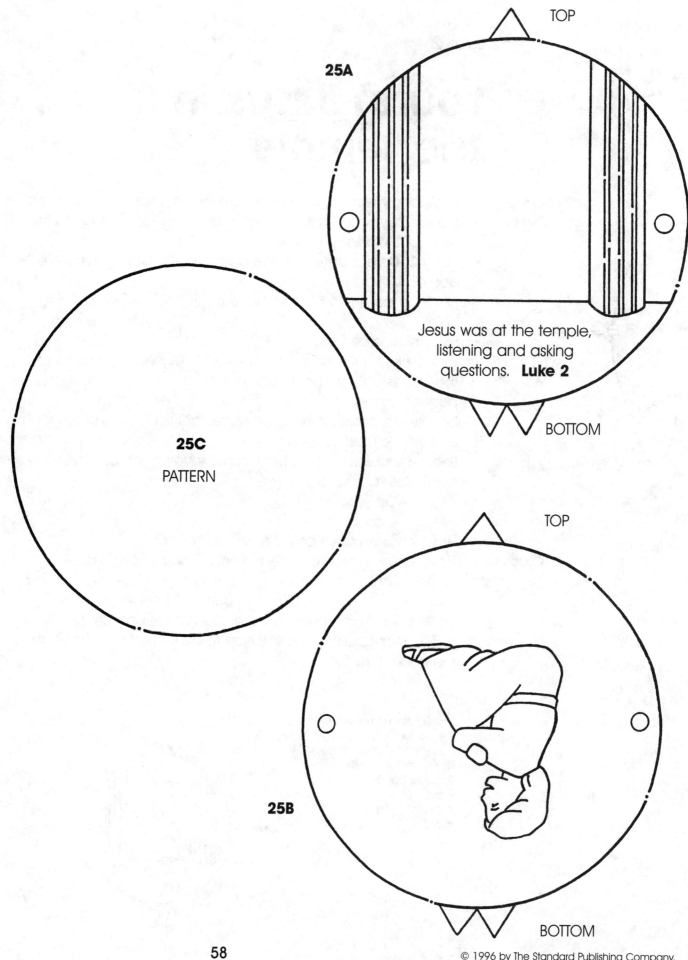

25A

TOP

Jesus was at the temple,
listening and asking
questions. **Luke 2**

BOTTOM

25C

PATTERN

TOP

25B

BOTTOM

© 1996 by The Standard Publishing Company.
Permission is granted to reproduce this page for ministry purposes only—not for resale.

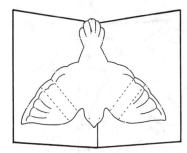

Jesus' Baptism

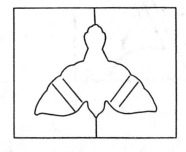

1

Before Class

- Photocopy reproducible page onto white, heavyweight copy paper.
- Score all fold lines on dove **(26A).** Cut out each piece.
- Fold and crease one sheet of light blue construction paper in half. This is your card.

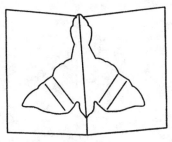

2

In Class

- Have children color **26B.**
- Glue the underside of both wing tabs. Center dove on card, aligning center creases of dove with card. See **1.**
- Pull body of dove out by making a mountain fold. Flip the tips of wings up (valley fold). See **2.** Close card and press.
- Glue **26B** on outside of card.
- When children open their cards, the dove pops out.

Materials for one activity
1 sheet light blue construction paper
1 sheet white, heavyweight copy paper
scissors
glue stick
crayons

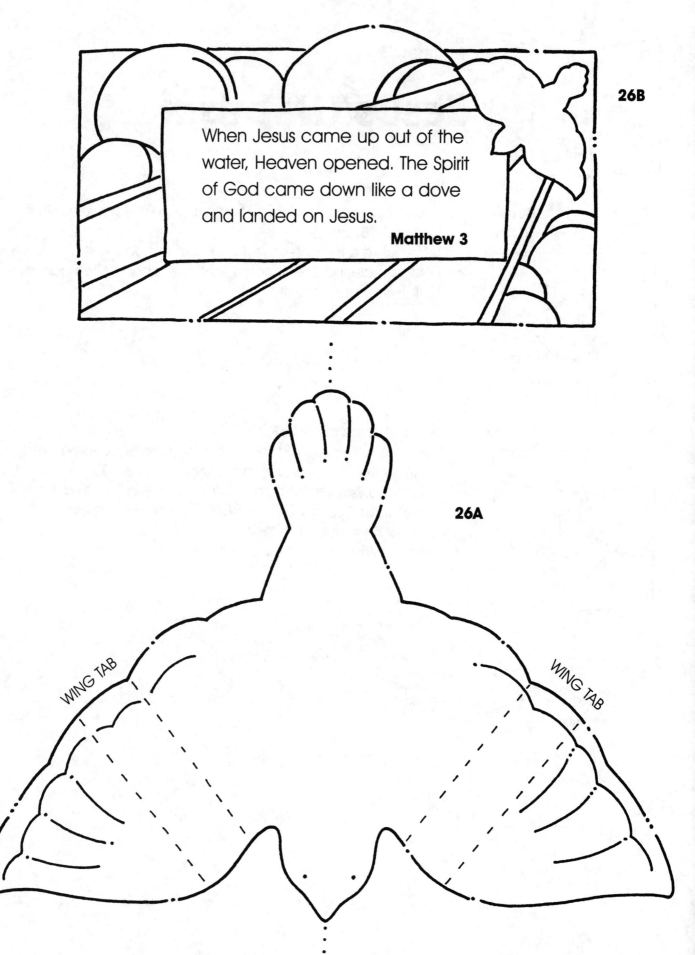

26B

When Jesus came up out of the water, Heaven opened. The Spirit of God came down like a dove and landed on Jesus.

Matthew 3

26A

WING TAB

WING TAB

© 1996 by The Standard Publishing Company.
Permission is granted to reproduce this page for ministry purposes only—not for resale.

Jesus Called Twelve

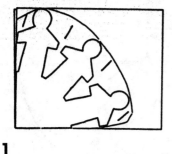

1

Before Class

- Photocopy reproducible page. Cut out **27A** along the outline. Cut out **27B,** cutting along the straight lines and a curve just beyond the tops of heads.
- Fold one sheet of any color, heavyweight copy paper in fourths. Line up the corner of pattern of apostles **(27B)** with the folded corner of the copy paper. Staple **27B** on top of the folded paper between outlines of the heads. This will make the pattern and paper stay in place and cutting will be easier. See **1.** Cut out along the outlines of the apostles.
- When cut out shape is opened, it will be a circle with body shapes representing the apostles around it. See **2.** Scoring the circle, will make it easier for children to fold up figures.

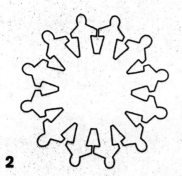

2

In Class

- Have children color Jesus **(27A).**
- With apostle circle opened flat, glue the back of **27A** and center it in the apostle circle.
- Have children stand each apostle up around Jesus, one by one.

Materials for one activity
1 sheet copy paper
1 sheet any color, heavyweight copy paper
stapler
scissors
glue stick
crayons

27A

Jesus called them

one by one.

Luke 6

27B

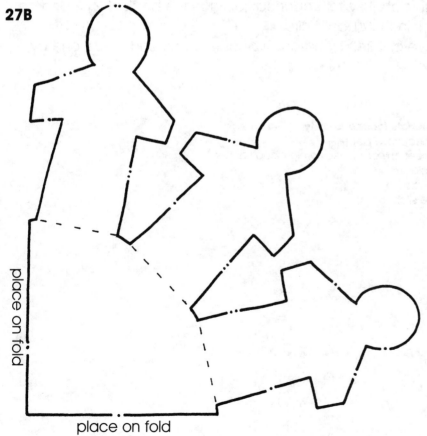

place on fold

place on fold

62

© 1996 by The Standard Publishing Company.
Permission is granted to reproduce this page for ministry purposes only—not for resale.

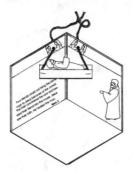

Lame Man Healed

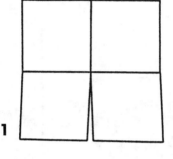

1

Before Class

- Photocopy reproducible page onto white, heavyweight copy paper. Place a strip of tape on the back of the man **(28C)** for stability. Cut out each piece.
- Fold room **(28A)** in half on fold line (valley).
- Cut a sheet of construction paper into a 9-inch square. Fold paper in fourths. Open paper. Cut along the bottom fold to the center. See **1.**
- Cut two lengths of yarn, 6 inches each. Tie a small knot on one end of each. Tape knotted ends of yarn onto the bed **(28B)** at the **X**s. See **2.** Fold the bed on the fold line (valley) over knots and staple on the knots. (This is an easy way to securely fasten yarn to paper.)

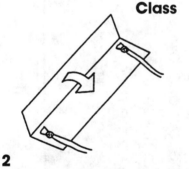

2

In Class

- Have children color each piece.
- Glue room onto the top sections of the square of construction paper. Align the center crease in the room to the center crease on the construction paper.
- Punch holes in the top of the room where indicated.
- Stand construction paper room up (all folds are valley). Glue one bottom section on top of the other. See **3.**
- Thread the two ends of yarn through holes in top of room, leaving bed inside room. Tie a knot in back. See **3.**

Preschool

Before class, glue room onto square of construction paper. Punch holes. Follow rest of instructions to complete.

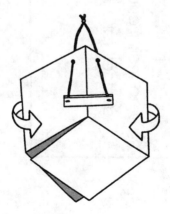

3

Materials for one activity
1 sheet construction paper
1 sheet white, heavyweight copy paper
12-inch length of yarn
stapler
hole punch
tape
scissors
glue stick
crayons

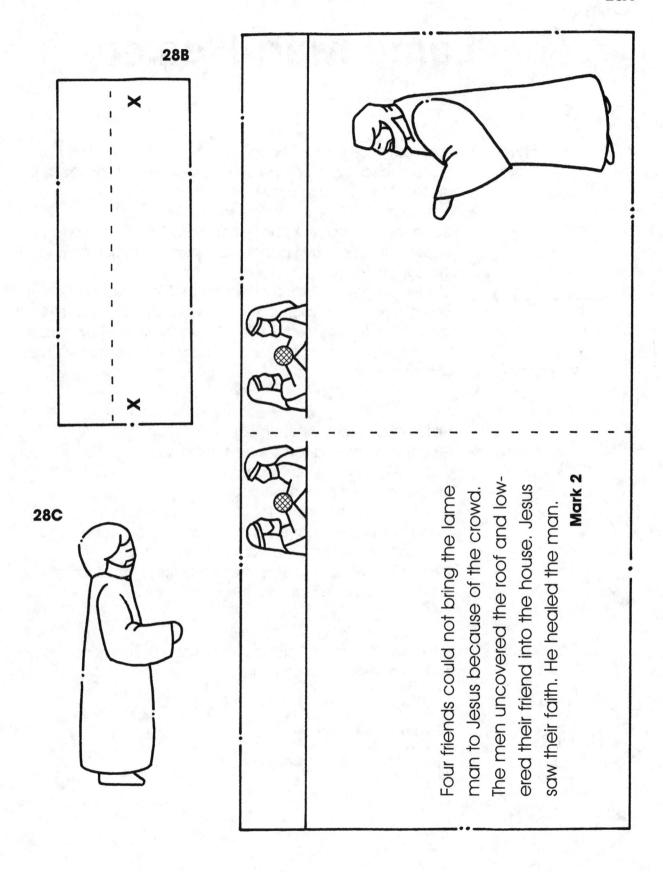

28B

28C

X

X

Four friends could not bring the lame
man to Jesus because of the crowd.
The men uncovered the roof and low-
ered their friend into the house. Jesus
saw their faith. He healed the man.

Mark 2

© 1996 by The Standard Publishing Company.
Permission is granted to reproduce this page for ministry purposes only—not for resale.

Be Wise

Before Class

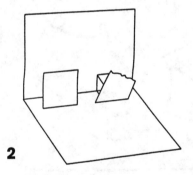

1

- Photocopy reproducible page and the box supports **(29A)** from this page onto white, heavyweight copy paper. Cut out each piece.
- Fold and crease one sheet of construction paper in half. This is your card.
- Follow instructions **Box Support** (page 7). See **1.**

In Class

- Have children color each piece.
- Follow instructions **Box Support** (page 7). Have children glue houses **(29B)** to supports. See **2.**
- Glue cloud **(29C)** on card above houses. Glue rock **(29D)** under standing house and sand **(29E)** under broken house.
- Glue **29F** on outside of card.
- When children open their cards, both houses stand up.

2

Materials for one activity
1 sheet construction paper
2 sheets white, heavyweight copy paper
scissors
glue stick
crayons

29A

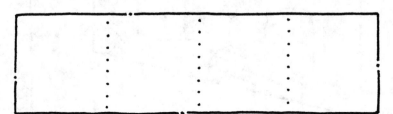

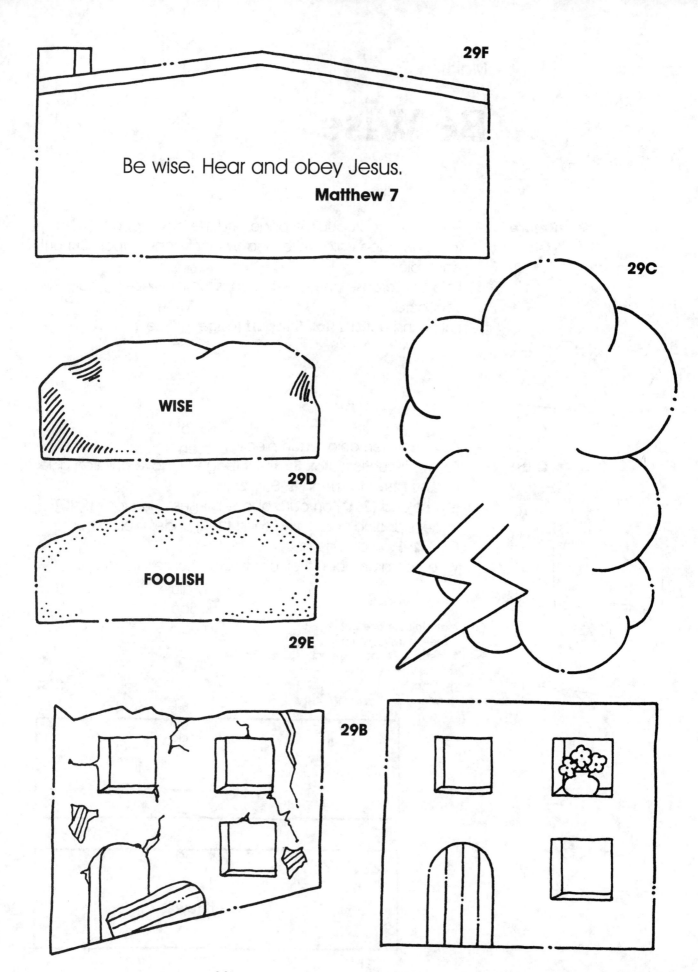

29F

Be wise. Hear and obey Jesus.
Matthew 7

29C

WISE

29D

FOOLISH

29E

29B

© 1996 by The Standard Publishing Company.
Permission is granted to reproduce this page for ministry purposes only—not for resale.

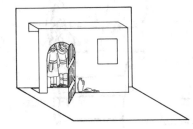

Healing Centurion's Servant

Before Class
- Photocopy reproducible page and **30C** from this page onto white, heavyweight copy paper. Score all fold lines (tabs and door hinge) on house **(30A).** Cut out each piece.
- Use an X-Acto knife to cut out window and around door. Stop at fold line at the hinge.
- Fold and crease one sheet of construction paper in half. This is your card.

In Class

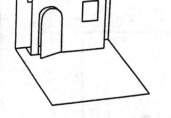

- Have children color each piece.
- Follow instructions **Box Stand-Ups** (page 6). See **1.**
- Open door and have children glue men **(30B)** inside at door on card.
- Glue **30C** to outside of card.
- When children open their cards, the house stands up. Open the door to see men.

1

Preschool

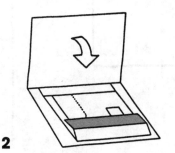

Before class, have bottom tab on activity glued to card and lay it down with top two sections folded back. See **2.** Close card. In class, have children glue top tab facing up. Close card and press. Follow rest of instructions to complete.

Materials for one activity
1 sheet construction paper	scissors
2 sheets white, heavyweight copy paper	glue stick
X-Acto knife	crayons

2

30C

A Roman soldier had great faith. He told Jesus,
"Say the word. My servant will be healed."

Matthew 8

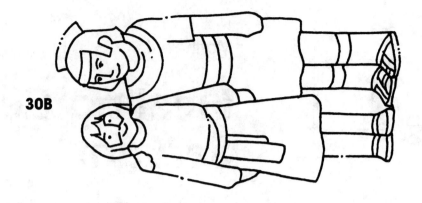

30B

30A

TOP TAB

cut out

BOTTOM TAB

68

© 1996 by The Standard Publishing Company.
Permission is granted to reproduce this page for ministry purposes only—not for resale.

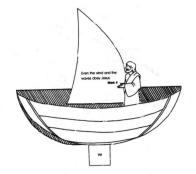

Jesus Calms the Sea

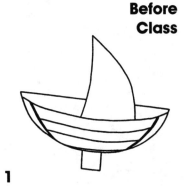

1

Before Class

- Photocopy reproducible page and the sail **(31D)** from this page onto white, heavyweight copy paper. Place a strip of tape on the back of the figure **(31A)** for stability. Cut out each piece.
- Trace the boat base **(31C)** onto folded construction paper. Make sure to align *place on fold* edge of pattern with folded edge of construction paper. Cut out.

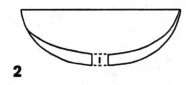

2

In Class

- Have children color each piece.
- Glue bottom edge of boat **(31B)** to boat base. Glue only outer edge, keeping top open.
- Glue bottom edge of sail onto the boat base. See **1**.
- Bend tabs at bottom of boat base under and staple one on top of the other. See **2**.
- Place Jesus in the boat to sleep. Rock the boat for a storm. Stand Jesus up to calm the seas.

Materials for one activity
1 sheet construction paper
2 sheets white, heavyweight copy paper
stapler
scissors
glue stick
crayons

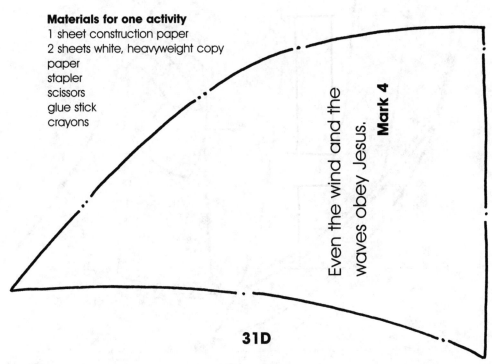

Even the wind and the waves obey Jesus. **Mark 4**

31D

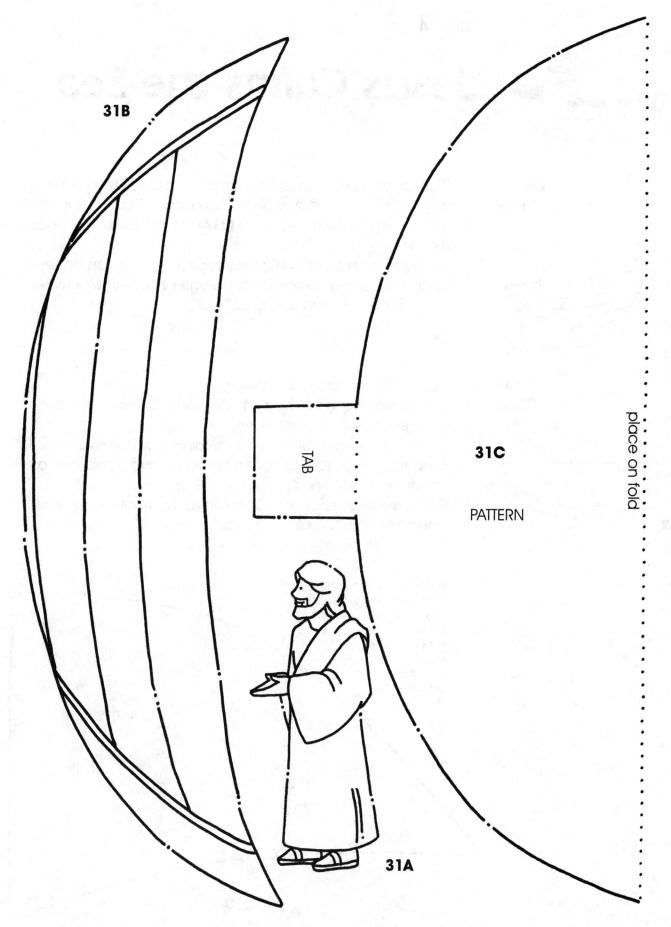

31B

31C

PATTERN

TAB

place on fold

31A

© 1996 by The Standard Publishing Company.
Permission is granted to reproduce this page for ministry purposes only—not for resale.

Luke 9

Jesus Feeds 5,000

Before Class

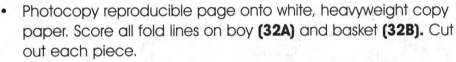

- Photocopy reproducible page onto white, heavyweight copy paper. Score all fold lines on boy **(32A)** and basket **(32B).** Cut out each piece.
- Fold all dot/dash lines (mountain/valley) on boy and basket.
- Glue outer edges of the basket together. Fold closed. See **1.** Glue only outside edges, keeping top open. Fish and bread **(32C)** will be slipped in the top.
- Fold and crease one sheet of construction paper in half. This is your card.

In Class

- Have children color each piece.
- Open card. Glue the back of boy, but do not get glue on hand area. Place boy on card, aligning center crease of boy with center crease of card. See **2.**
- Lay the flat basket on boy. Place a spot of glue on both areas on basket where hands will be placed. Fold hands over basket. Align placement. See **3.** Pull basket out as a mountain fold.
- Slip fish and bread inside basket.
- Glue **32D** to outside of card.
- When children open their cards, the basket of fish and bread pops out.

Preschool   Before class, glue boy onto the card. Follow the rest of the instructions to complete.

Materials for one activity
1 sheet construction paper
1 sheet white, heavyweight copy paper
scissors
glue stick
crayons

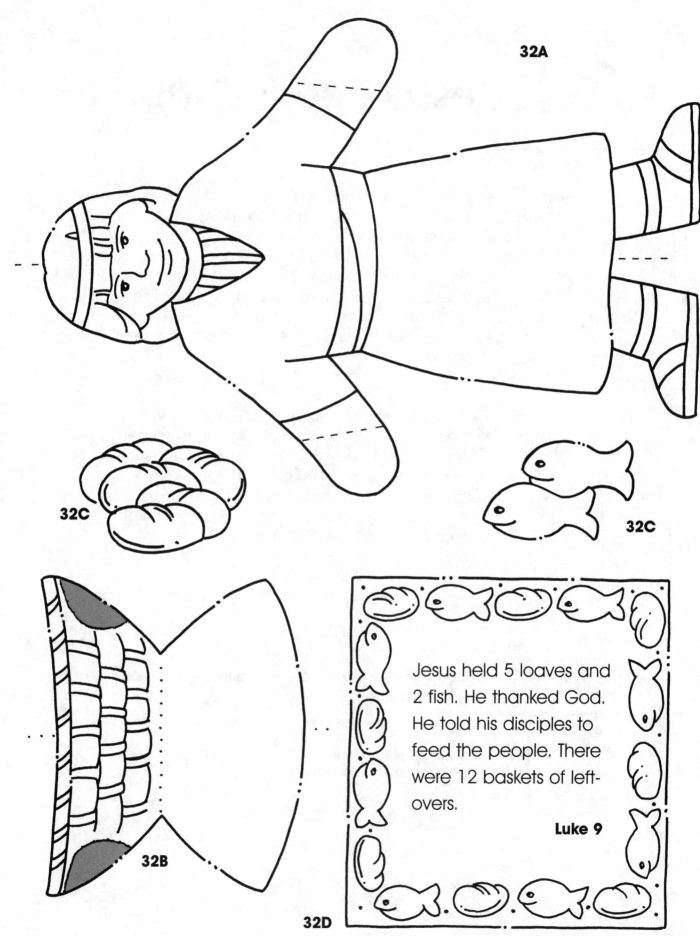

32A

32C

32C

32B

Jesus held 5 loaves and
2 fish. He thanked God.
He told his disciples to
feed the people. There
were 12 baskets of left-
overs.

Luke 9

32D

© 1996 by The Standard Publishing Company.
Permission is granted to reproduce this page for ministry purposes only—not for resale.

Peter Walks on Water

Before Class

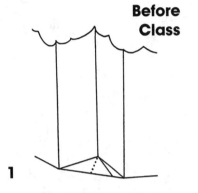

- Photocopy reproducible page onto white, heavyweight copy paper. Score all fold lines on waves **(33A).** Cut out each piece.
- Fold and crease one sheet of construction paper in half. This is your card.
- Glue tabs on waves together, one on top of the other. See **1.** (Viewed from back.) The dotted line on tabs, shown on **1,** will (mountain) fold up behind the waves when card is folded flat and will form a flat base when the card is opened. See **2.**
- Open card. Glue the back of the waves, except for the top 1/2 inch of the waves and the center folded area. Place on the card. Align center creases and bottom edges. See **3.** Close card and press.
- The waves do not extend all the way to the side edges of the construction paper card. Trim the card to fit. See **3.**
- When children open their cards, the center wave pops out.

In Class

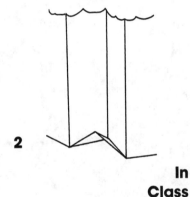

- Have children color each piece. If some of the creases are smashed from coloring, just pop the waves back into place.
- Glue **33D** on outside of card.
- Have children slip Jesus' feet **(33B)** behind waves on the right side.
- Start with Peter **(33C)** slipped behind the waves on the left side. As Peter walks toward Jesus, move Peter to the center of the card and drop him into the popped-out space in the waves. When Peter asks Jesus for help, slip the figure behind the waves on the right side next to Jesus.

Materials for one activity
1 sheet construction paper
1 sheet white, heavyweight copy paper
scissors
glue stick
crayons

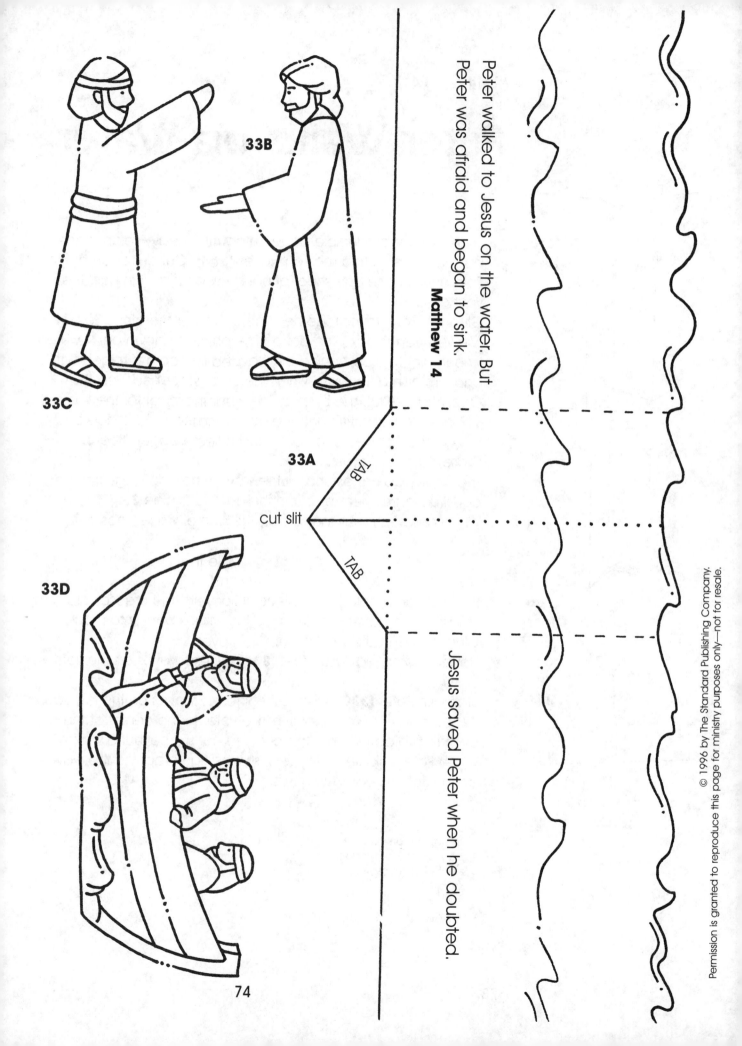

33B

33C

33A

TAB

TAB

cut slit

33D

Peter walked to Jesus on the water. But Peter was afraid and began to sink.

Matthew 14

Jesus saved Peter when he doubted.

74

© 1996 by The Standard Publishing Company.

Permission is granted to reproduce this page for ministry purposes only—not for resale.

Blind Man Healed

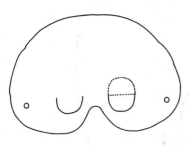

Before Class

- Photocopy reproducible page and **34B** from this page onto white, heavyweight copy paper. Before cutting out, turn copied paper over and tape the back where holes are to be punched and behind the **U**-shape under eyes to prevent tearing. Cut out each piece.
- Use an X-Acto knife to cut **U**-shaped lines under each eye on the mask **(34A).** See illustration. Dotted line indicates one eye flap folded back behind mask.
- Punch two holes where indicated near the edge of mask. Cut two 12-inch lengths of yarn. Tie yarn ends in holes. If you prefer, use a 6-inch length of elastic thread tied to each hole on the mask.

In Class

- Have children color each piece.
- Glue **34B** to back of mask.
- Tie or slip mask on a child's head while the mask eyes are down. Let children pretend to be blind.
- Remove mask and have child color eyelids brown. (Jesus put mud on the eyes.)
- Put mask back on. Pretend to wash eyes. Bend eye flaps up inside the mask. Now child can see! (Jesus healed the blind man.)

Materials for one activity
2 sheets white, heavyweight copy paper
24-inch length of yarn or 6-inch length of elastic thread
X-Acto knife
hole punch
tape
scissors
glue stick
crayons

34B

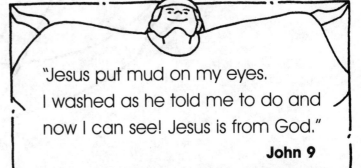

"Jesus put mud on my eyes.
I washed as he told me to do and
now I can see! Jesus is from God."
John 9

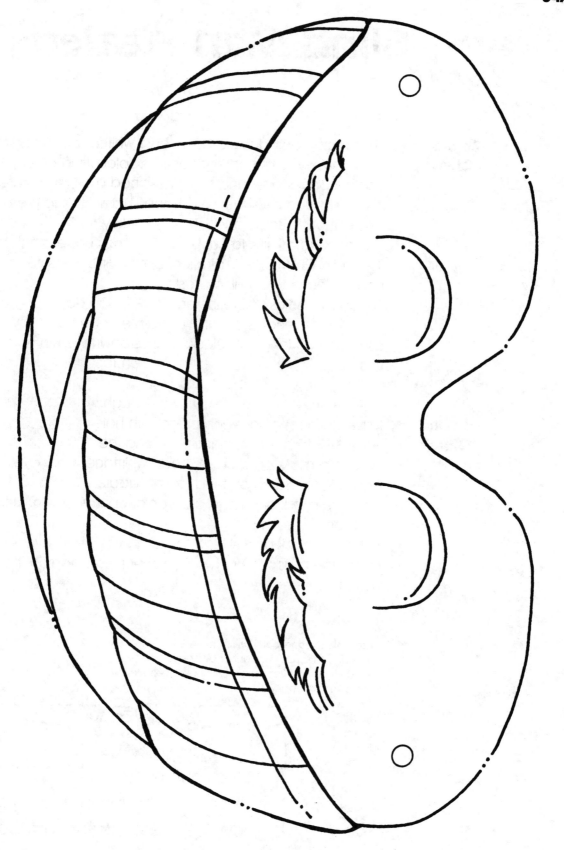

© 1996 by The Standard Publishing Company.
Permission is granted to reproduce this page for ministry purposes only—not for resale.

Luke 10

Good Samaritan

Before Class

1

- Photocopy reproducible page onto white, heavyweight copy paper. Before cutting out, turn the copied paper over and put strips of tape over holes to be punched and slits to be cut on donkey parts **35B, 35C,** and **35D.** Cut out each piece.
- Use an X-Acto knife to cut slits on donkey **(35B).** Punch holes.

In Class

2

- Have children color each piece.
- Bend tail **(35D)** at fold line and glue down.
- With legs **(35C)** facing forward, fasten top holes to tail with paper fasteners. See **1.**
- Coming from the back, slip legs through slits on donkey to the front. Align bottom holes on legs with holes in donkey and secure with paper fasteners, opening them in the back. See **2.**
- Glue bottom edge of saddle **(35E).** Attach to donkey. See **3.**
- Slip man **(35A)** on donkey behind saddle. Have children walk donkey to an inn,* holding head and pulling and pushing the tail.

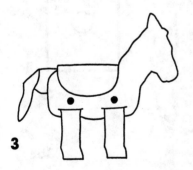

3

Materials for one activity
1 sheet white, heavyweight copy paper
X-Acto knife
4 paper fasteners (brads)
tape
scissors
glue stick
crayons
* Make an inn from a small cardboard box.

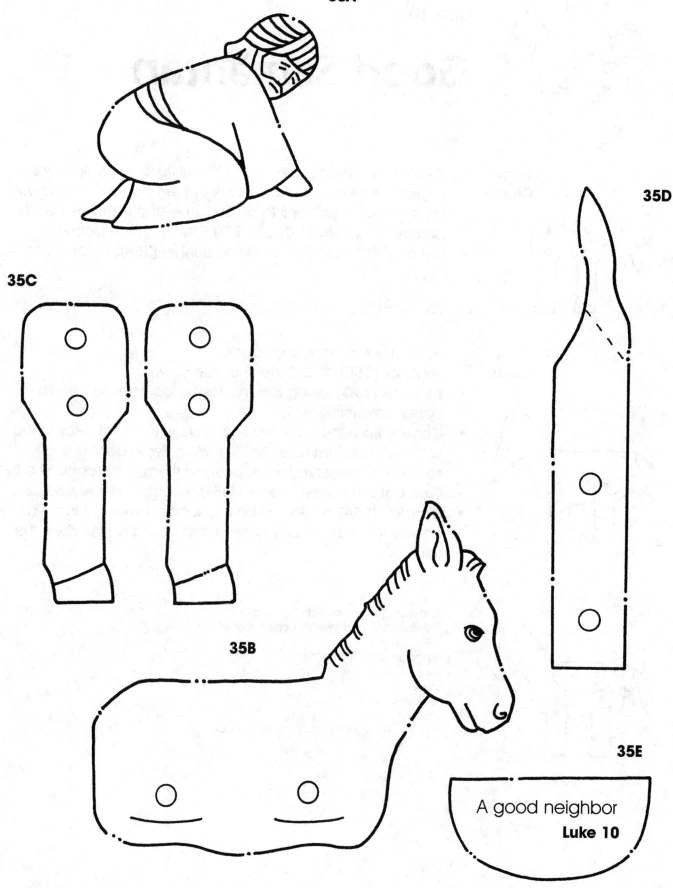

35A

35D

35C

35B

35E

A good neighbor
Luke 10

© 1996 by The Standard Publishing Company.
Permission is granted to reproduce this page for ministry purposes only—not for resale.

Luke 11

Our Father in Heaven

Before Class

- Photocopy reproducible page onto white, heavyweight copy paper. Before cutting out, turn the copied paper over and put strips of tape along the cutting line at the "thought" on the child's head **(36A).**
- Turn over and using an X-Acto knife, cut the top and bottom slits where indicated. Cut out each piece.

In Class

- Have children color each piece.
- Slip strip **(36B)** through slits on head. See illustration (viewed from back). Bring end tabs around back, making a circle, and tape. Make sure to cover all corners with tape on tabs so strip will scroll smoothly.

Materials for one activity
1 sheet white, heavyweight copy paper
X-Acto knife
tape
scissors
crayons

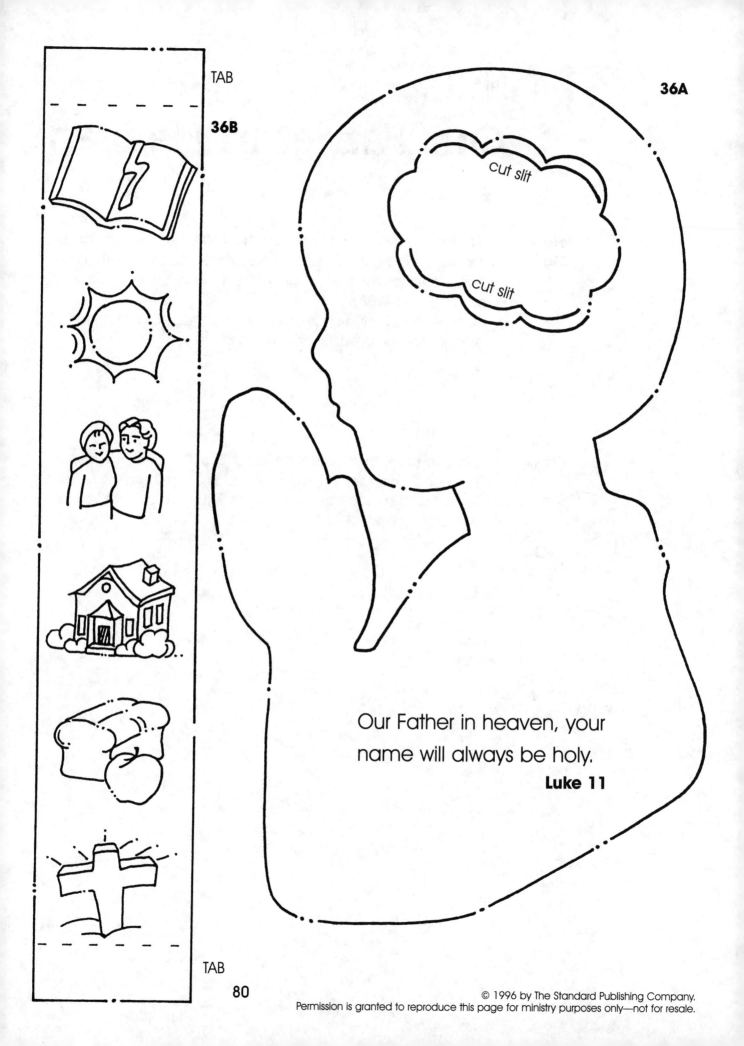

TAB

36B

36A

cut slit

cut slit

Our Father in heaven, your
name will always be holy.

Luke 11

TAB

80

© 1996 by The Standard Publishing Company.
Permission is granted to reproduce this page for ministry purposes only—not for resale.

John 11

Jesus Raises Lazarus

Before Class

- Photocopy reproducible page and wrapped Lazarus **(37A)** from this page onto white, heavyweight copy paper. Score all fold lines. Do not score Lazarus **(37B)**, only the dotted lines on either side. Cut out.
- Use an X-Acto knife to cut out area around head on **37B**.
- Fold tabs back and tape together on wrapped Lazarus.

In Class

- Have children color each piece.
- Tell the story and use the visual to demonstrate. For example:
    Jesus' friend Lazarus had died and people had buried him while Jesus was away. *(Lay the paper (37B) flat with the wrapped Lazarus (37A) slipped on. Continue.)*
    When Jesus came back to Bethany, Martha and Mary each said to Jesus, "Lord, if You had been here, our brother would not have died." But they knew that whatever Jesus asked of God, God could give. People went to the tomb. Jesus told them to move the stone. Jesus thanked God for hearing. Then He called for Lazarus to come out. *(Fold paper in place, at dotted line so 37B stands up with wrapped Lazarus still on. Tape tab to back of paper.)* See **1**.
    Lazarus came out of the tomb. Jesus said, "Take off his grave cloths and let him go." *(Take wrapped cloths (37A) from Lazarus.)* See **2**.

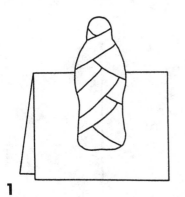

1

2

Materials for one activity
2 sheets white, heavyweight copy paper
X-Acto knife
tape
scissors
crayons

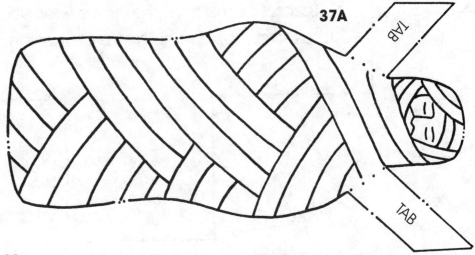

37A

TAB

TAB

Mary and Martha said to Jesus, "Lord, if you had been here, our brother would not have died."

Lazarus came from the grave wrapped in cloth. Jesus said, "Take off his grave clothes and let him go."

John 11

TAB

82

Mary and Martha said to Jesus, "Lord, if you had been here, our brother would not have died."

cut out   cut out

Lazarus came from the grave wrapped in cloth. Jesus said, "Take off his grave clothes and let him go."

John 11

TAB

82

© 1996 by The Standard Publishing Company.
Permission is granted to reproduce this page for ministry purposes only—not for resale.

Luke 17

One Said, "Thank You"

Before Class

- Photocopy figure **(38A)** and clothing **(38B)** from this page onto white, heavyweight copy paper. Cut out each piece.
- Accordion fold a sheet of heavyweight copy paper lengthwise. The folds will be approximately 2 1/8-inches wide making five folds. Cut off excess beyond the last fold.
- Trace figure onto the folded paper twice as shown. See **1.** If you staple the folded paper near each head, arm, and leg, figures will stay in place and cutting will be easier and faster. Cut out both. Do not cut at dotted lines of hands and feet.
- Tape two sets of five figures together, making ten. See **2.** Tape the seam on both sides and cut off excess tape. Accordion fold the figures.

1

In Class

- Have children color the clothes.
- Glue clothes on the top figure. Draw a happy face on that figure only.
- Turn the set of ten right side down and have children draw faces on the nine who did not return to say "Thank You" (indicating that they went away from Jesus).

2

Materials for one activity
2 sheets white, heavyweight copy paper
stapler
tape
scissors
glue stick
crayons

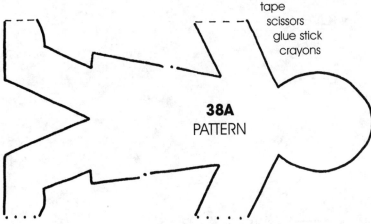

38A
PATTERN

38B

Jesus said, "Did I not heal all ten men?"
Luke 17

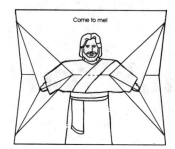

Come to me!

Matthew 19

Children Come to Jesus

Before Class

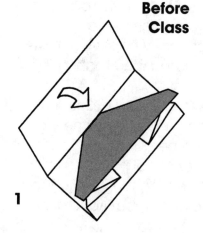

1

- Photocopy reproducible page onto white, heavyweight copy paper. Score all fold lines. Cut out **39** along the outline.
- Fold in half, then quarters. Open back up to a half fold. With Jesus facing up, crease each fold line as indicated by dot (mountain) and dash (valley). This is similar to **Pop-Ups in a Picture** (page 5), but is self-contained and has two **V**-folds. See **1**.
- Pull Jesus' arms to the inside of the card. Fold paper flat. See **2**.

In Class

2

- Have children color Jesus and the children.
- With card folded in half and Jesus' arms folded in, turn card face down. Glue area indicated on bottom section of card. See **1**. Close card making sure edges and quarter folds are aligned.
- When children open the cards, Jesus opens His arms to them. See **2**.

Materials for one activity
1 sheet white, heavyweight copy paper
scissors
glue stick
crayons

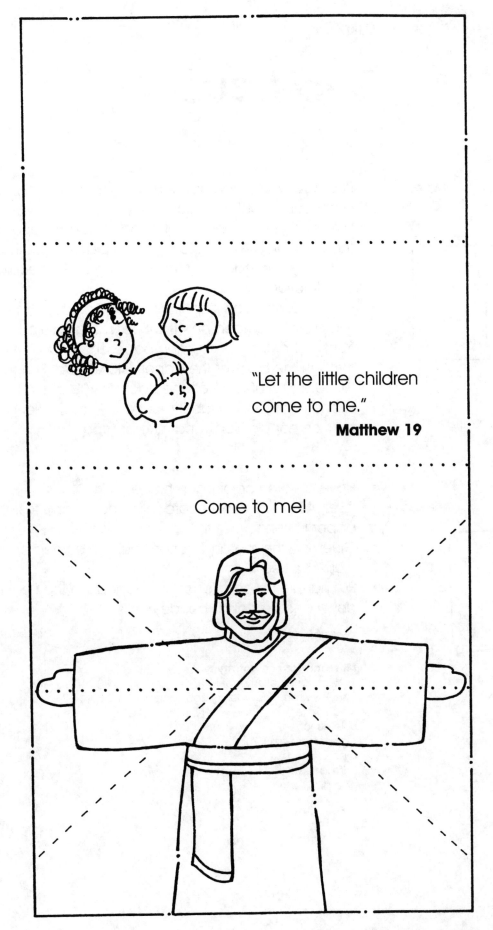

"Let the little children come to me."
Matthew 19

Come to me!

© 1996 by The Standard Publishing Company.
Permission is granted to reproduce this page for ministry purposes only—not for resale.

Luke 19

Zaccheus

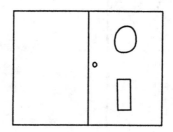

1

- Photocopy both reproducible pages onto white, heavyweight copy paper. Cut out each piece.
- Fold and crease one sheet of construction paper in half. Glue the back of **40A** and place on folded construction paper. The *place on fold* edge of **40A** must align with the folded edge of construction paper.
- Open construction paper. Use an X-Acto knife to cut out the two areas indicated on **40A**. See **1**. Make sure to cut only the front half of the construction paper sheet. Do not cut holes through the back of the paper. Close card. Punch hole.
- Place a strip of tape on the back of **40B** at the base of the tabbed handle for stability. Cut out. Punch hole. Fold both side tabs on handle back and glue or tape.

In Class

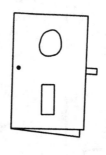

2

- Have children color each piece.
- Insert **40B** into folded card, align holes, and fasten with a paper fastener.
- Glue only the top and bottom outside corners of card to keep it closed. See **2**.
- Pull handle up and Zaccheus appears in the tree. Pull handle down and he stands beside Jesus.

Materials for one activity
1 sheet construction paper
2 sheets white, heavyweight copy paper
X-Acto knife
hole punch
1 paper fastener (brad)
tape
scissors
glue stick
crayons

cut out

place on fold

cut out

"Zaccheus, come down quickly," said
Jesus. "I'll go to your house today."

Luke 19

© 1996 by The Standard Publishing Company.
Permission is granted to reproduce this page for ministry purposes only—not for resale.

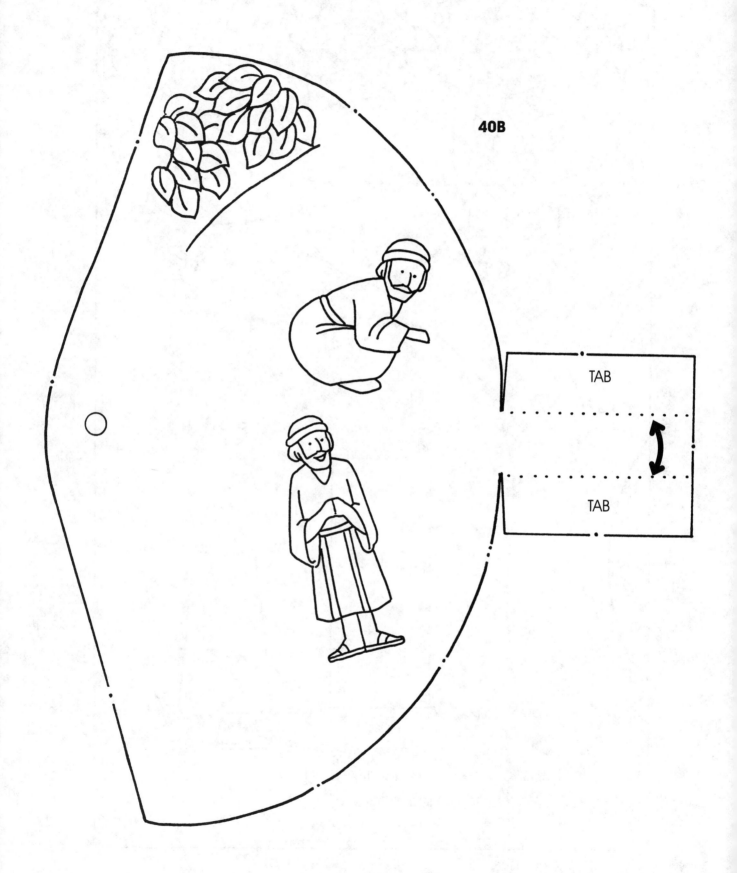

40B

TAB

TAB

© 1996 by The Standard Publishing Company.
Permission is granted to reproduce this page for ministry purposes only—not for resale.

Luke 19

Jesus Enters Jerusalem

Before Class

1

- Photocopy both reproducible pages onto white, heavyweight copy paper. Score all fold lines on donkey **(41A).** Cut out each piece.
- Use an X-Acto knife to cut out areas on donkey where indicated.
- Follow instructions **Stand-Up Animals** (page 6). See **1.** (Note: bottom tabs are not shown.)
- Fold and crease one sheet of construction paper in half. This is your card.

In Class

- Have children color each piece.
- Glue the back of Jesus' legs **(41B).** Place on donkey.
- Open card. Glue the outside of one of the tabs on donkey. Place tab in middle of card with bottom edge of tab aligned with center crease of card. See **2.** With donkey lying flat, glue the tab facing up. Close and press.
- Glue coats **(41C)** and palm branches **(41D)** on inside of card in front of donkey's path. Save some to glue outside.
- Glue **41E** on outside of card. Glue coats and the branches in front of **41E.**
- When children open their cards, Jesus riding a donkey stands up. See **3.**

2

Preschool

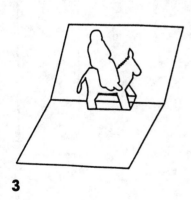

3

Before class, have donkey formed and one tab attached to card. The children can color donkey and Jesus. Glue Jesus on donkey and lay down flat. Glue tab facing up. See **2.** Close card and press. Follow rest of instructions to complete.

Materials for one activity
1 sheet construction paper
2 sheets white, heavyweight copy paper
X-Acto knife
scissors
glue stick
crayons

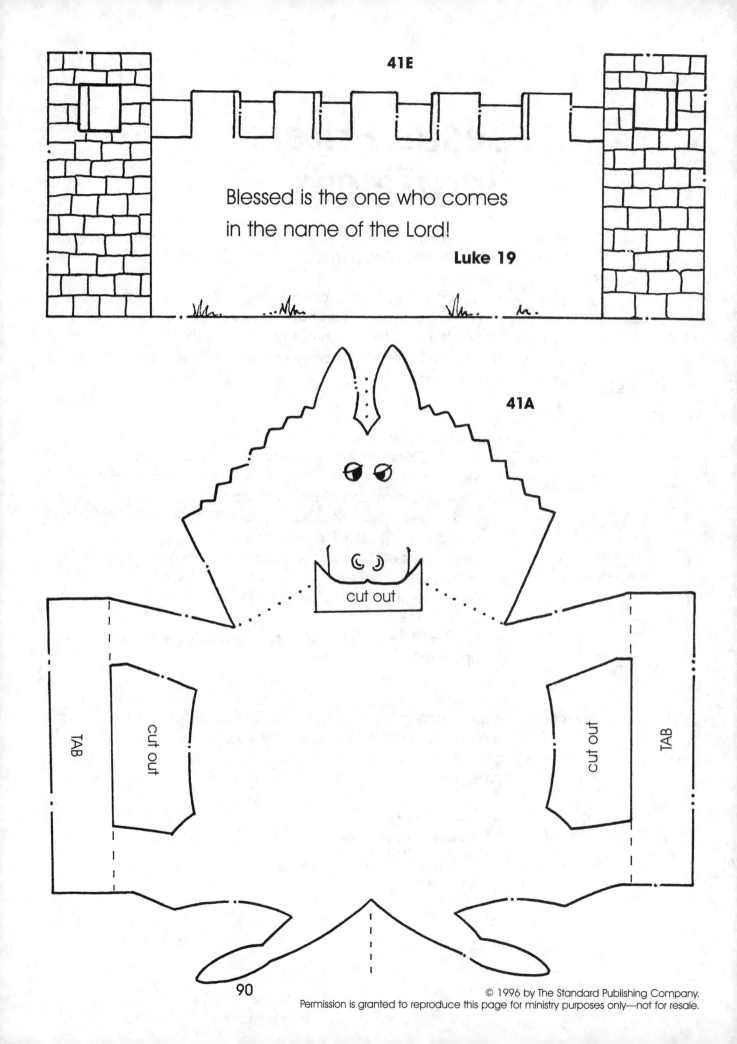

41E

Blessed is the one who comes
in the name of the Lord!

Luke 19

41A

cut out

cut out

TAB

cut out

cut out

TAB

© 1996 by The Standard Publishing Company.
Permission is granted to reproduce this page for ministry purposes only—not for resale.

41B

41C

41D

© 1996 by The Standard Publishing Company.
Permission is granted to reproduce this page for ministry purposes only—not for resale.

Luke 22

The Upper Room

Before Class

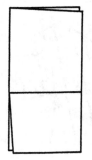

1

- Photocopy reproducible page and **42B** from this page onto white, heavyweight copy paper. Score all fold lines on **42A,** down center, across floor, and window hinges. Cut out each piece. Cut the bottom of the center fold where indicated, up to fold line. See **1.**
- Use an X-Acto knife to cut slits at top, middle, and bottom of window on **42A.**

In Class

2

- Have children color each piece.
- From the back, center Jesus in the open window and tape.
- Fold the upper room (all valley folds) so that it stands up and the bottom right section laps over the bottom left section. See **2.**
- Glue between the sections so the upper room stands.

Materials for one activity
2 sheets white, heavyweight copy paper
X-Acto knife
tape
scissors
glue stick
crayons

42B

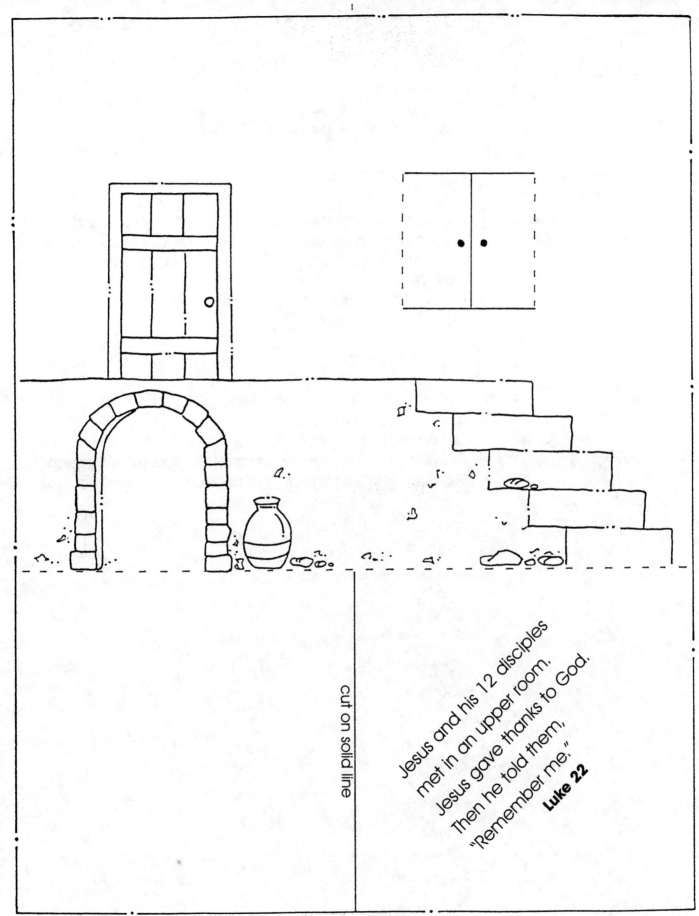

cut on solid line

Jesus and his 12 disciples met in an upper room. Jesus gave thanks to God. Then he told them, "Remember me." **Luke 22**

© 1996 by The Standard Publishing Company.
Permission is granted to reproduce this page for ministry purposes only—not for resale.

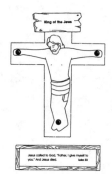

Luke 23

"It Is Finished"

Before Class
- Photocopy reproducible page onto white, heavyweight copy paper. Turn copied paper over and put strips of tape on the small slit areas on Jesus' hands and feet **(43A),** and on the cross **(43B).** Cut out each piece.
- Use an X-Acto knife to cut slits on hands and feet, and on cross, where indicated.

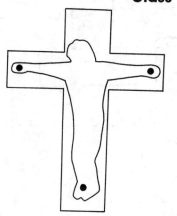

In Class
- Have children color each piece.
- Use paper fasteners to attach Jesus to cross. See illustration.
- Glue the back of cross to a sheet of black construction paper.
- Glue sign **(43C)** on top of cross and **43D** at the base of the cross.

Materials for one activity
1 sheet black construction paper
1 sheet white, heavyweight copy paper
X-Acto knife
3 paper fasteners
tape
scissors
glue stick
crayons

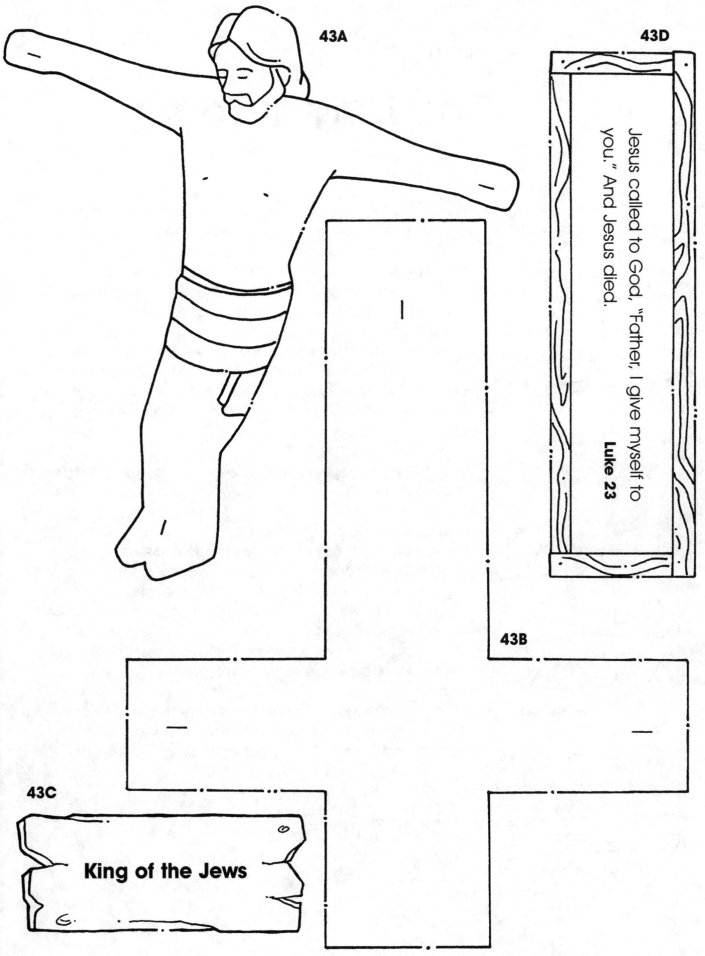

43A

43D

Jesus called to God, "Father, I give myself to you." And Jesus died.

Luke 23

43B

43C

King of the Jews

© 1996 by The Standard Publishing Company.
Permission is granted to reproduce this page for ministry purposes only—not for resale.

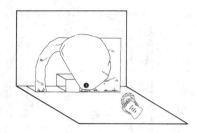

The Empty Tomb

Before Class

- Photocopy both reproducible pages onto white, heavyweight copy paper. Score all fold lines on tomb **(44A).** Cut out each piece.
- Use an X-Acto knife to cut out the entrance to tomb.
- Glue stone **(44B)** to a scrap of construction paper for support. Cut out. Punch all holes on the stone and tomb.
- The bottom three small sections *(front, top, back)* on the tomb will form the bench on which the body was placed. Glue the bottom section on the word *front* only. Using all mountain folds, bring that section back and around to the wrong side of the tomb. Align holes and press. This will make an open-ended box (bench) that will be partially visible in the tomb entrance. See **1.** (View from back.)
- Fold and crease one sheet of construction paper in half. This is your card.

1

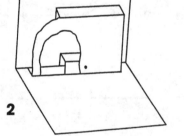

In Class

- Have children color each piece.
- Follow instructions **Box Stand-Ups** (page 6). See **2.**
- Attach stone to tomb with a paper fastener. You must stick your finger inside the bench to open the fastener ends.
- Glue angels **(44C)** to the inside of card below tomb and **44D** to the outside of card.
- When card is opened, the tomb stands up and children can roll the stone to see the empty tomb.

2

Preschool

Before class, have the bottom tab on the tomb glued to card with top two sections folded back. See **3.** Have children glue top tab. Close card and press. Follow rest of instructions to complete.

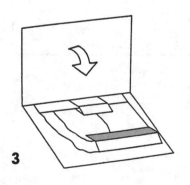

Materials for one activity
1 sheet construction paper
2 sheets white, heavyweight copy paper
scrap of construction paper
X-Acto knife
hole punch
1 paper fastener (brad)
scissors
glue stick
crayons

3

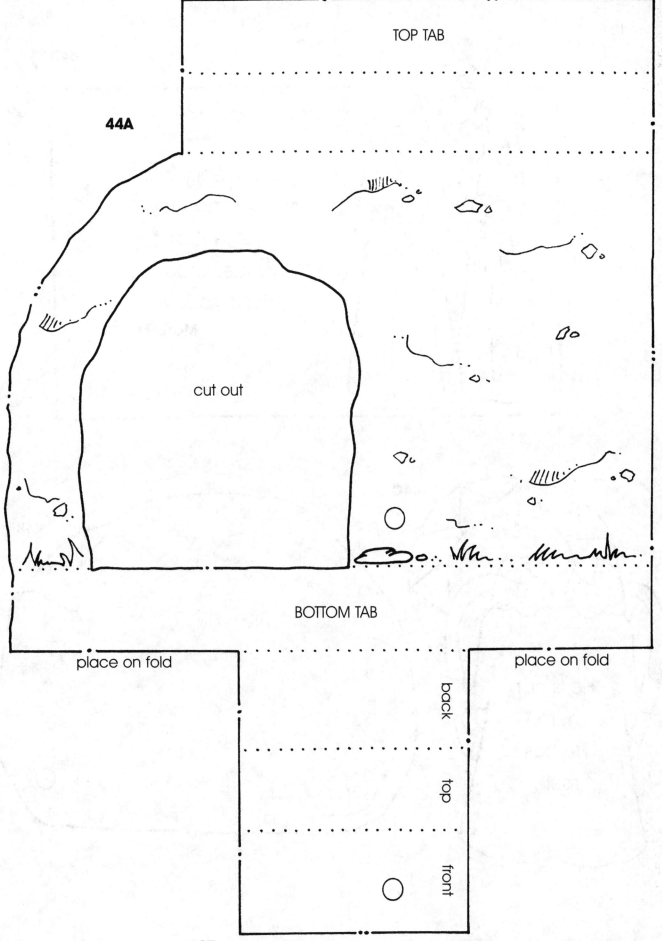

TOP TAB

44A

cut out

BOTTOM TAB

place on fold

place on fold

back

top

front

© 1996 by The Standard Publishing Company.
Permission is granted to reproduce this page for ministry purposes only—not for resale.

44D

Very early in the morning they came to put spices around Jesus' body.

Mark 16

44C

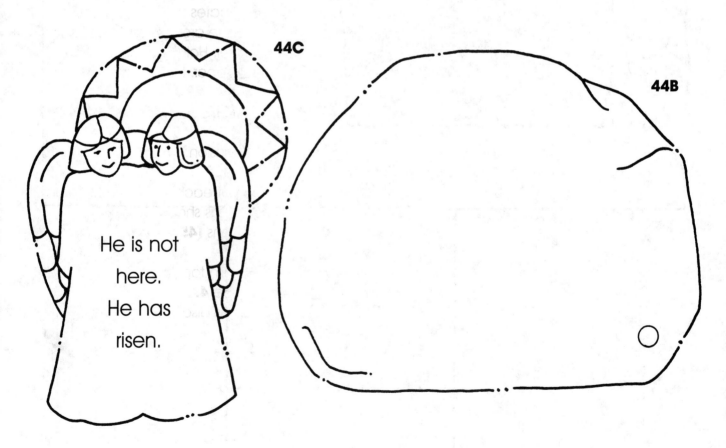

He is not here. He has risen.

44B

© 1996 by The Standard Publishing Company.
Permission is granted to reproduce this page for ministry purposes only—not for resale.

The Ascension

Before Class

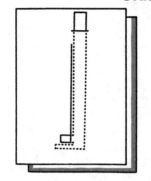

2

- Photocopy both reproducible pages onto white, heavyweight copy paper. Cut out each piece.
- Using cloud **(45A)** as a pattern, cut two clouds from white construction paper. Using slide **(45B)** as a pattern, cut one slide from poster board, adding to the top so that the slide is 10 3/4 inches long.
- Using a ruler and X-Acto knife, cut one sheet of light blue construction paper as shown in the diagram. See **1** on page 101. Turn paper over and tape both ends of both slits for stability and to prevent tearing.
- From the back, slip the top of slide, with arrow through the horizontal slit at top. (The extension at the bottom of slide will face to your left.) Next, slip extension area marked *glue 45C* through center slit. See **2.** (Dashed line indicates the position of the slide on the back of the paper.) Glue around all four edges of another sheet of construction paper. Holding slide in place, align both sheets of construction paper. Press. Don't get glue around the slide.

3

In Class

- Have children color each piece.
- Put a spot of glue on the slide extension *(glue 45C)* of slide and place Jesus **(45C)** on it. See **3.**
- Glue along the long, straight side of each cloud where indicated, and place each on the paper as shown. See **3.**
- Glue angels **(45E)** and word balloons **(45D)** on either side of Jesus as shown. See **3.**
- Gently pull clouds up and slide them together, joining at the **X** where indicated on the pattern. See **4.**
- Pull the top of the slide so that Jesus disappears into the clouds. Lay clouds flat for storage.

4

Materials for one activity
2 sheets blue construction paper
1 sheet white construction paper
2 sheets white, heavyweight copy paper
1 10 3/4-by-2 1/4-inch piece of poster board
X-Acto knife
tape
scissors

glue stick
crayons

© 1996 by The Standard Publishing Company.
Permission is granted to reproduce this page for ministry purposes only—not for resale.

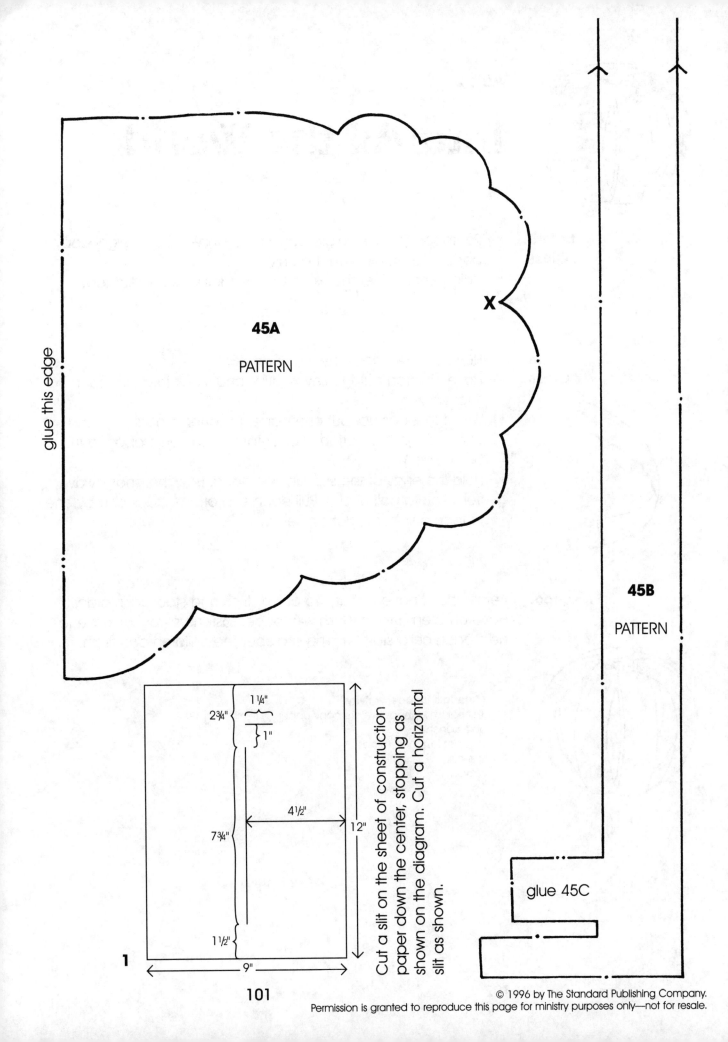

45A

PATTERN

glue this edge

X

45B

PATTERN

glue 45C

2¾" 1¼"

1"

4½"

7¾"

12"

1½"

1

9"

Cut a slit on the sheet of construction paper down the center, stopping as shown on the diagram. Cut a horizontal slit as shown.

101

© 1996 by The Standard Publishing Company.
Permission is granted to reproduce this page for ministry purposes only—not for resale.

Acts 2

Into All the World

Before Class

- Photocopy reproducible page onto white, heavyweight copy paper. Cut out the outline only.
- Hole punch seven holes on both edges where indicated.

In Class

- Have children color the water on **46.**
- Have children cut the seven strips and stack them in order, 1 through 7.
- With right sides up, put one paper fastener through top and one through the bottom. Paper fasteners should open to the back. See **1.**
- Hold the ends of the strips in one hand. Bow the ends away from you (a half-circle). Pull each strip off the stack one by one to form a sphere (globe). See **2.**

1

Preschool

Before class, have activity **46** cut in strips and stacked in order. Have children attach them with paper fasteners. You will have to help each child start forming a globe. The children can finish.

Materials for one activity
1 sheet white, heavyweight copy paper
hole punch
2 paper fasteners (brads)
scissors
crayons

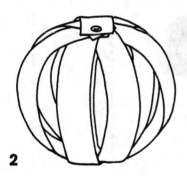

2

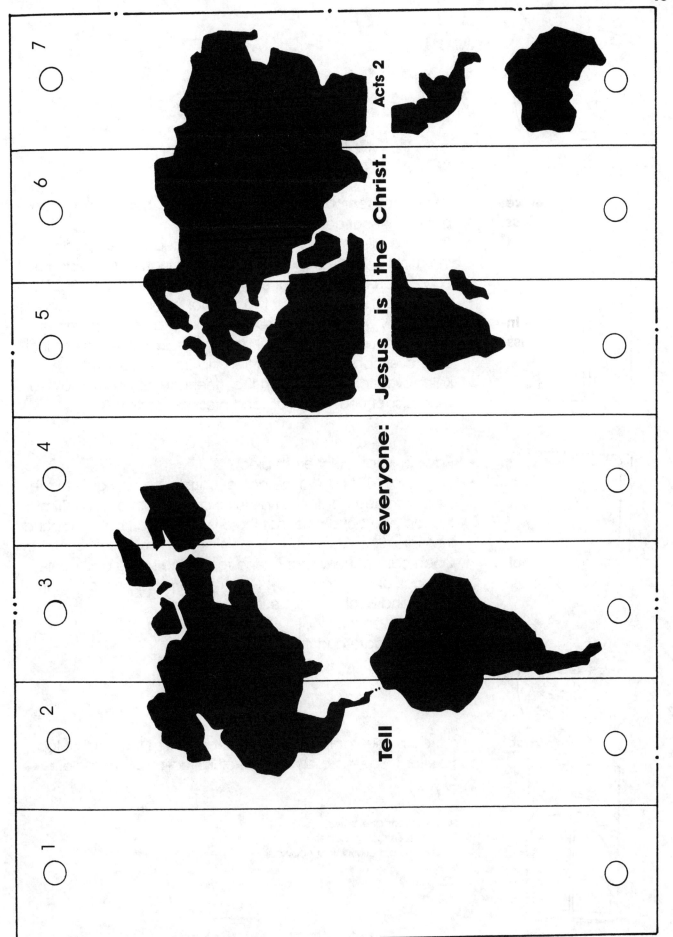

© 1996 by The Standard Publishing Company.
Permission is granted to reproduce this page for ministry purposes only—not for resale.

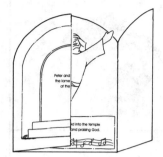

Acts 3

A Lame Beggar Healed

Before Class
- Photocopy reproducible page onto white, heavyweight copy paper. Cut out each piece.
- The card will be construction paper folded so the opening is in the middle. Score construction paper 3 inches from each side edge, then fold in so that edges meet in the middle. See **1.**
- Make a paper spring. Cut two strips of paper (1/2-by-5-inches) from copy paper. Glue a spot on one end of a strip and lay the other strip on it at a right angle. See **2.** Shaded areas indicate overlapping strips. Fold first strip up over second strip. Keep overlapping one then the other until all paper is folded. Glue a spot under top flap and press down. See **3.**

1

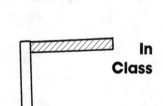

In Class
- Have children color each piece.
- Cut gates **(47A)** down the center on the line and glue to the front of folded card. Align pictures across front of card. Trim at the top and bottom so that there is a half-inch border around the gate. See **4.**
- Open card. Glue a spot on the top of the spring and center it on back of the man **(47B).** Glue a spot on the bottom of the spring and center it on the inside of card.
- Glue **47C** on the inside.
- Open the gate and the man leaps for joy.

2

3

Preschool Before class, glue gates to outside of card. Trim the card at top and bottom. See **4.** Follow the rest of instructions to complete.

Materials for one activity
1 sheet construction paper
1 sheet white, heavyweight copy paper
scissors
glue stick
crayons

4

47A

Peter and John saw
the lame man sitting
at the temple gate. **Acts 3**

47C

He walked into the temple
leaping and praising God.

47B

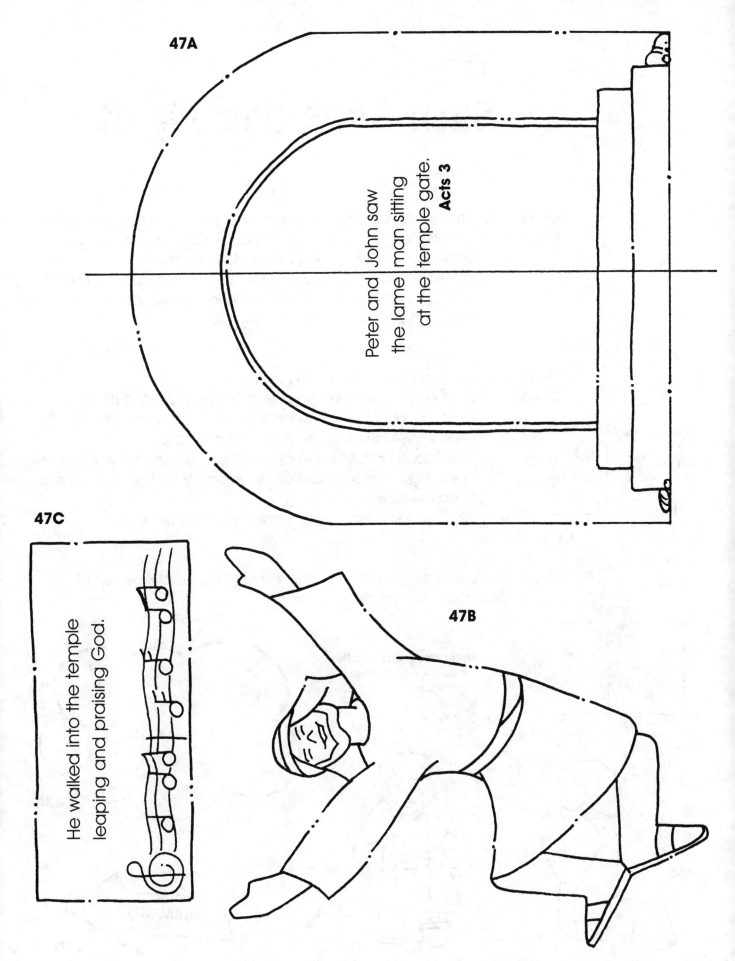

105

© 1996 by The Standard Publishing Company.
Permission is granted to reproduce this page for ministry purposes only—not for resale.

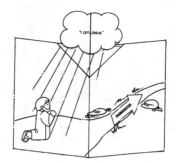

Saul Sees the Light

Before Class
- Photocopy reproducible page and the patterns on this page onto white, heavyweight copy paper. Cut out each piece.
- Score fold line on cloud **(48A).** Fold (mountain).
- Follow instructions on page 30 (#12) to construct card **(48E).** See **1.** Notice that there is no extension on the **V**-fold. The cloud will be glued on as the extension.

In Class

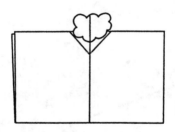

- Have children color each piece.
- Glue angry Saul **(48B)** on outside where indicated **(B).** Glue sorry Saul **(48C)** on inside left in the "light" where indicated **(C).** Glue sign **(48D)** on inside right on the road **(D).**
- Glue along bottom edge of cloud and place on the **V**-fold on card. Align center crease on cloud and **V**-fold on card. See **2.** Keep the cloud within the **V**-fold.
- When children open their cards, the cloud pops up.

1

Preschool

Before class, glue cloud in the **V**-fold **(48E).** Follow the rest of directions to complete.

Materials for one activity
2 sheets white, heavyweight copy paper
scissors
glue stick
crayons

2

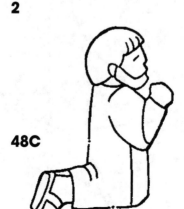

48C

48B

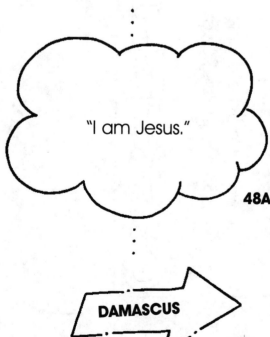

"I am Jesus."

48A

DAMASCUS

48D

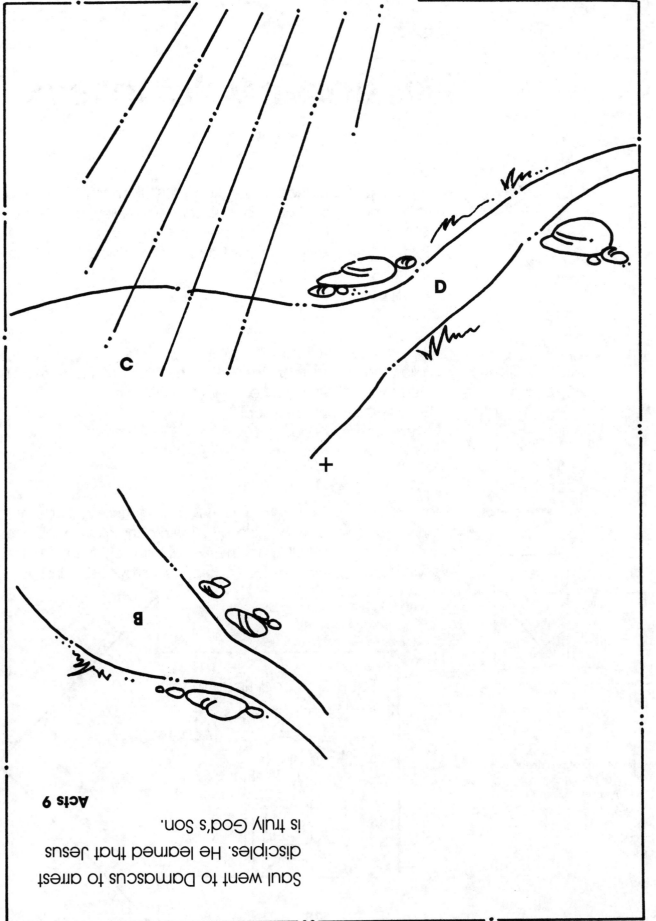

C

D

B

+

Saul went to Damascus to arrest
disciples. He learned that Jesus
is truly God's Son.

Acts 9

© 1996 by The Standard Publishing Company.
Permission is granted to reproduce this page for ministry purposes only—not for resale.

Acts 16

Missionary Journeys

Before Class

- Photocopy reproducible page and **49C** from this page onto white, heavyweight copy paper. Score all (valley) fold lines on **49A** and **49B.** Cut out each piece.
- Fold and crease one sheet of construction paper in half. This is your card.

In Class

- Have children color each piece.
- Follow instructions **Pop-Ups With Tabs** (page 5). Place **49A** first, then place **49B** two inches in front of **49A.** See **1.**
- Glue **49C** on outside of card.
- When card is opened, people pop up.

1

2

Preschool

Before class, have both **49A** and **49B** glued to the right side of the inside of card. See **2.** In class, children can unfold people to color. Fold people back up as they were. Have children glue the two tabs facing up. Close card and press. Follow rest of instructions to complete.

Materials for one activity
1 sheet construction paper
2 sheets white, heavyweight copy paper
scissors
glue stick
crayons

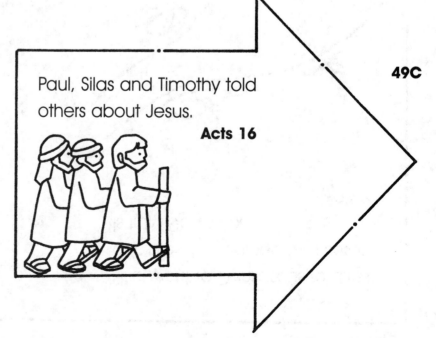

Paul, Silas and Timothy told others about Jesus.

Acts 16

49C

TAB
TAB

49B

Churches grew
larger each day.
Churches grew
stronger in faith.
TAB
TAB

© 1996 by The Standard Publishing Company.
Permission is granted to reproduce this page for ministry purposes only—not for resale.

Paul and Silas in Stocks

Before Class

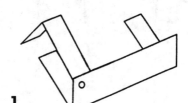

1

- Photocopy both reproducible pages onto white, heavyweight copy paper. Cut out each piece. Score and fold Paul and Silas **(50D)**.
- Glue **50A, 50B,** and **50C** to a half sheet of construction paper for stability. Cut out each piece. Punch holes.
- Score and (mountain) fold dot lines on **50B** and **50C**.
- Glue the tab with hole punched on **50C** to the back of **50B** aligning holes. See **1**.
- Fold and crease one sheet of construction paper in half. This is your card.
- Open card. Glue the tab on **50B**. Place it in the middle of card. Align the two back edges with the center crease of card.
- Lay **50B** flat forward. Glue the area marked *card tab* (on the support). Close card and press. See **2**.
- Open card. Attach **50A** to **50B** with paper fasteners. The long extension on **50A** will go behind **50B**. See **3**.
- When card is opened halfway, stock will stand. when card is flat, stock will be flat.

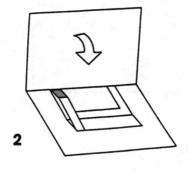

2

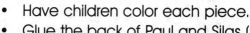

In Class

- Have children color each piece.
- Glue the back of Paul and Silas (above the waist). Do not glue legs. Place them so they are centered in stocks. Fold feet up and place in stocks; then slightly bend the knees. See **4**.
- Glue **50E** on outside of card and **50F** on inside of card.
- When card is opened, stocks stand up. Open and close the stocks.

3

Materials for one activity
1 sheet construction paper
1/2 sheet construction paper
2 sheets white, heavyweight copy paper
hole punch
1 paper fastener (brad)
scissors
glue stick
crayons

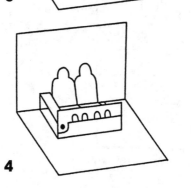

4

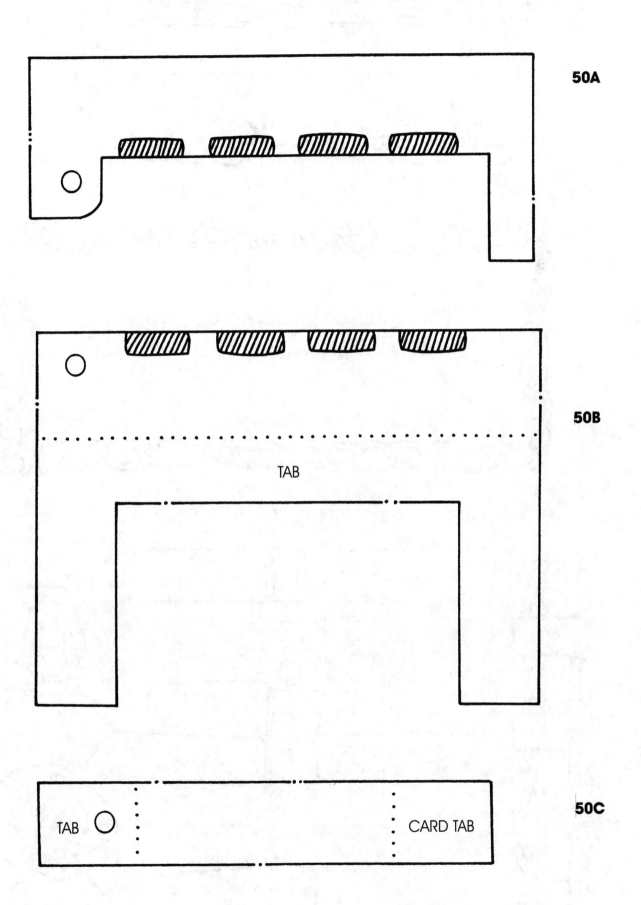

50A

50B

TAB

50C

TAB

CARD TAB

© 1996 by The Standard Publishing Company.
Permission is granted to reproduce this page for ministry purposes only—not for resale.

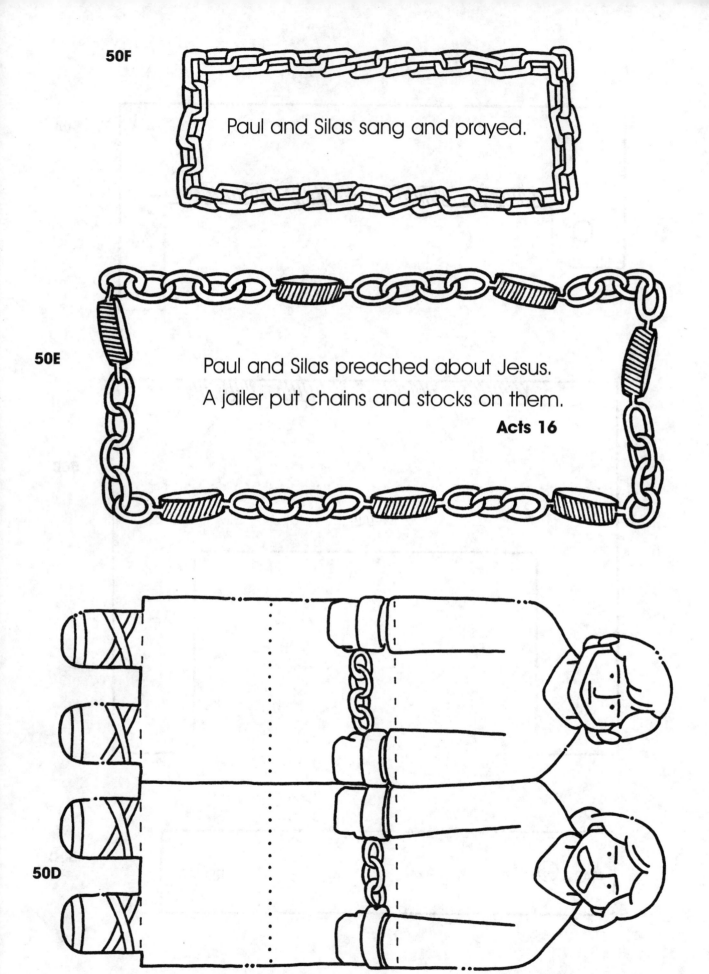

50F

Paul and Silas sang and prayed.

50E

Paul and Silas preached about Jesus.
A jailer put chains and stocks on them.

Acts 16

50D

112

© 1996 by The Standard Publishing Company.
Permission is granted to reproduce this page for ministry purposes only—not for resale.